★ SONGS OF ★
SPIRITUAL POWER

A Collection of Choice Gospel Songs for Church
Services, Sunday Schools, Revivals, Camp Meetings
and Home Mission Campaigns

Compiled by
JOHN T. BENSON

Eminent Composers

CHAS. H. GABRIEL	E. O. EXCELL	ROBERT HARKNESS
C. AUSTIN MILES	WM. J. KIRKPATRICK	J. R. SWENEY
H. L. GILMOUR	P. P. BLISS	GEO. BENNARD
HALDOR LILLENAS	CHAS. P. JONES	JAS. McGRANAHAN
MRS. C. H. MORRIS	R. E. WINSETT	J. LINCOLN HALL
JAS. M. BLACK	I. G. MARTIN	C. B. WIDMEYER
W. H. DOANE	I. A. SANKEY	N. B. HERRELL
B. D. ACKLEY	HAMP SEWELL	D. B. TOWNER

ROUND NOTES ONLY

POINT
CHURCH OF THE BRETHREN
Schellsburg, Pa. R. D.

Copyrighted 1947—All Rights Reserved

JOHN T. BENSON PUBLISHING CO.
NASHVILLE, TENNESSEE

PASTORS AND CHRISTIAN WORKERS may be assured that the 216 songs contained in this book have been selected for variety and for every type of church service. Indeed, songs to fit every occasion—for every mood of group and congregational singing, whether it be lively or slow and worshipful. It is important to note that a great many of the old stately Hymns of the church are included with the newer and more popularized Gospel songs.

EVANGELISTS will find "Songs of Spiritual Power" especially adapted for evangelistic campaigns with no impractical songs, but every song usable and "singable." In fact, this book may be carried into any community, no matter how strange or isolated with perfect assurance that songs are available which the crowds can sing with freedom and familiarity. A wide selection of invitation and altar songs make the book doubly serviceable in the field of evangelism.

JOHN T. BENSON

GLORIA PATRI.

DOXOLOGY.

THOS. KEN. (Old Hundred. L. M.) LEWIS BOURGEOIS.

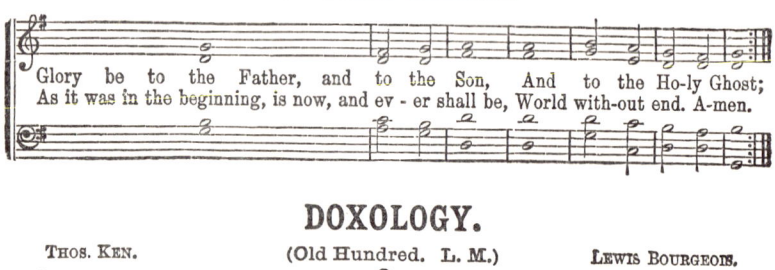

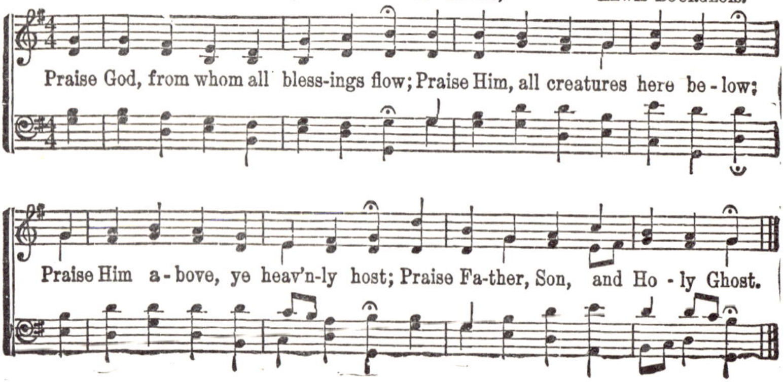

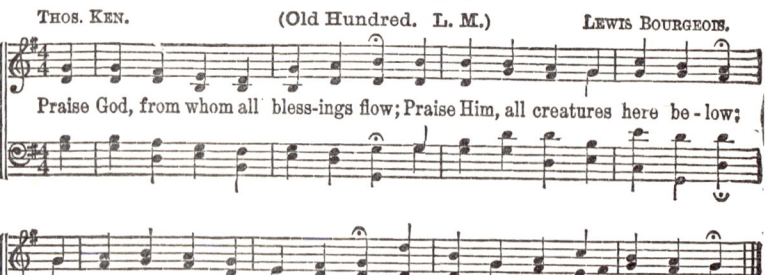

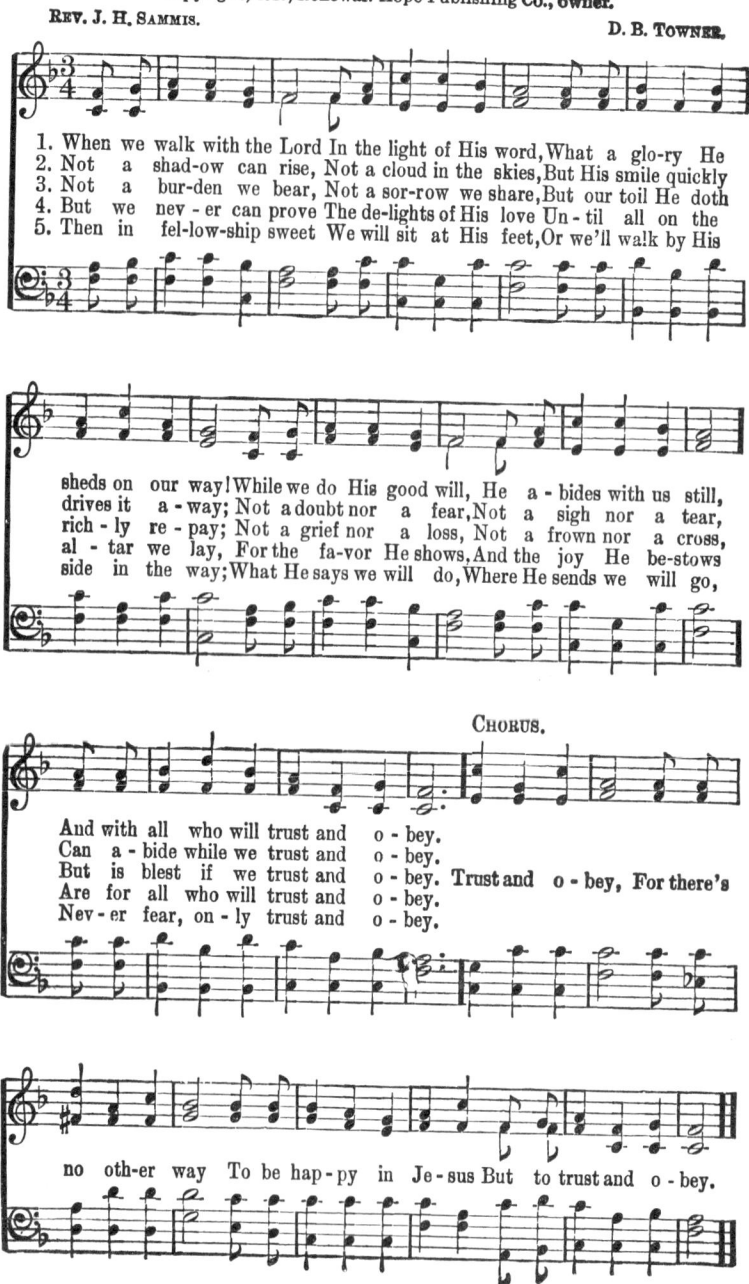

No. 3 Stepping in the Light.

Copyright, 1918, by Mrs. Wm. J. Kirkpatrick.
Hope Pub. Co., owner.

L. H. EDMUNDS. WM. J. KIRKPATRICK.

1. Try-ing to walk in the steps of the Sav-iour, Try-ing to fol-low our Sav-iour and King; Shap-ing our lives by his bless-ed ex-am-ple,
2. Pressing more closely to him who is lead-ing, When we are tempted to turn from the way; Trusting the arm that is strong to de-fend us,
3. Walking in footsteps of gen-tle for-bearance, Footsteps of faithfulness, mer-cy, and love, Look-ing to him for the grace free-ly promised,
4. Try-ing to walk in the steps of the Sav-iour, Upward, still upward we'll fol-low our Guide, When we shall see him, "the King in his beau-ty."

CHORUS.

Happy, how happy, the songs that we bring.
Happy, how happy, our prais-es each day.
Happy, how happy, our journey a-bove.
Happy, how happy, our place at his side.

How beautiful to walk in the steps of the Sav-iour, Stepping in the light, Stepping in the light; How beau-ti-ful to walk in the steps of the Saviour, Led in paths of light.

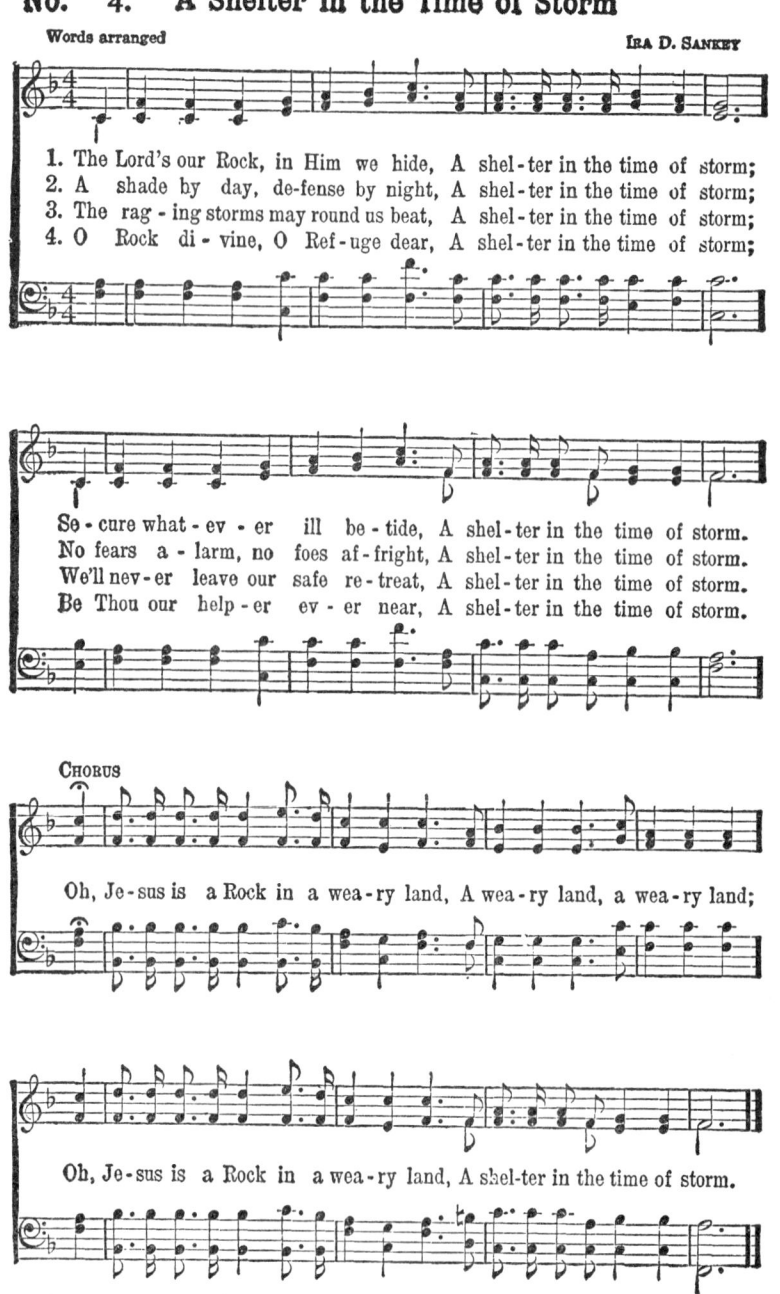

I Will Sing the Wondrous Story. Concluded.

Gath-ered by .... the crys-tal sea.
Gath-ered by the crys-tal sea.

No. 9   The Kingdom Coming.

Mrs. M. B. C. Slade.   R. M. McIntosh.

1. From all the dark pla - ces Of earth's heath-en ra - ces, Oh,
2. The sun - light is glanc - ing O'er ar - mies ad - vanc - ing, To
3. With shout - ing and sing - ing, And ju - bi - lant ring - ing, Their

see how the thick shad - ows fly! The voice of sal - va - tion A -
con - quer the king - doms of sin; Our Lord shall pos - sess them, His
arms of re - bell - ion cast down, At last ev - 'ry na - tion, The

D. S.—The earth shall be full of His
FINE.

wakes ev - 'ry na - tion, Come o - ver and help us, they cry.
pres - ence shall bless them, His beau - ty shall en - ter them in.
Lord of sal - va - tion Their King and Re - deem - er shall crown!

know - ledge and glo - ry, As wa - ters that cov - er the sea.
CHORUS.   D. S.

The kingdom is coming, Oh, tell ye the sto - ry, God's banner ex-alt - ed shall be!

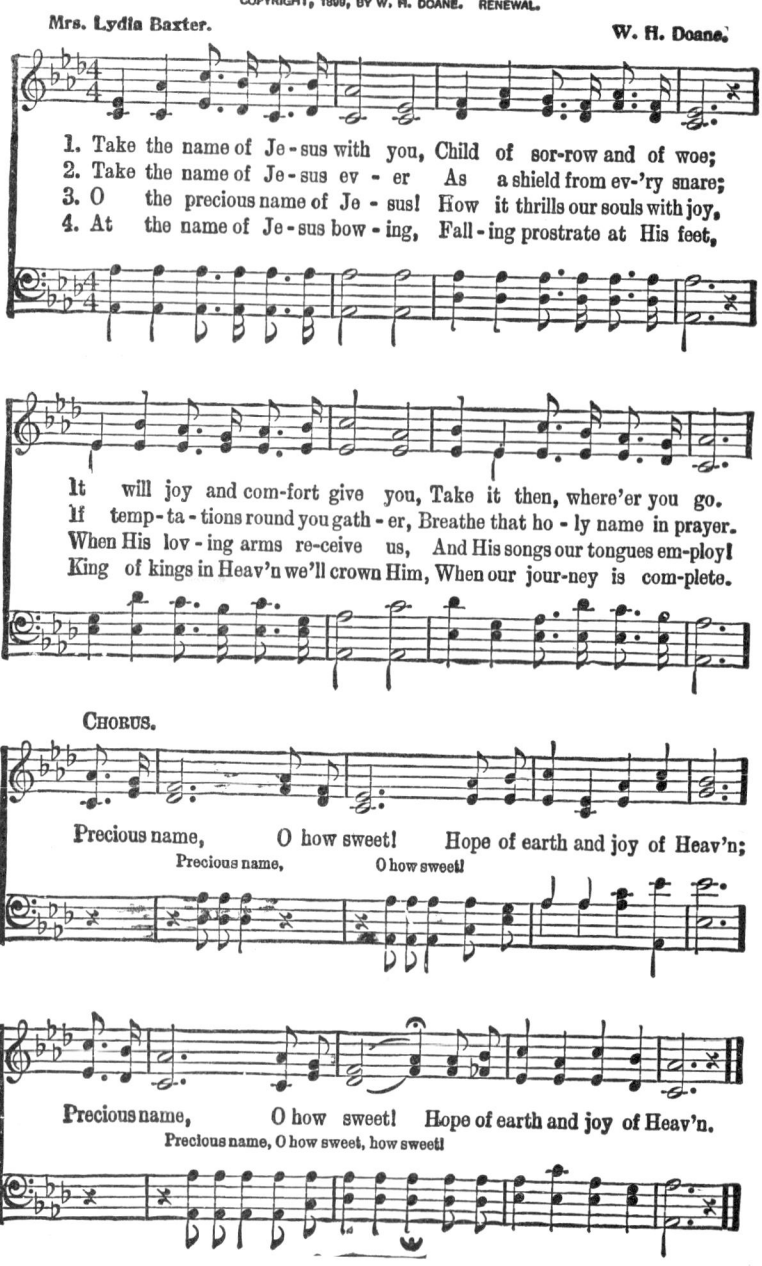

12 When the Mists Have Rolled Away

Annie Herbert. Arr.   Ira D. Sankey

1. When the mists have rolled in splendor From the beauty of the hills, And the sun-light falls in gladness On the river and the rills, We recall our Father's promise In the rain-bow of the spray: We shall know each other better When the mists have rolled a-way.

2. Oft we tread the path before us With a weary burdened heart; Oft we toil a-mid the shadows, And our fields are far a-part; But the Saviour's "Come, ye blessed" All our labor will re-pay, When we gather in the morning Where the mists have rolled a-way.

3. We shall come with joy and gladness, We shall gather round the throne; Face to face with those that love us, We shall know as we are known: And the song of our redemption Shall resound thro' endless day When the shadows have departed, And the mists have rolled a-way.

D. S.—In the dawn-ing of the morn-ing Of that bright and hap-py day, We shall know each oth-er bet-ter When the mists have rolled a-way.

Fine Chorus

We shall know . . . as we are known, ... Nev-er-more . . . to walk a-lone; . . . .
as we are known, Nev-er-more to walk a-lone;

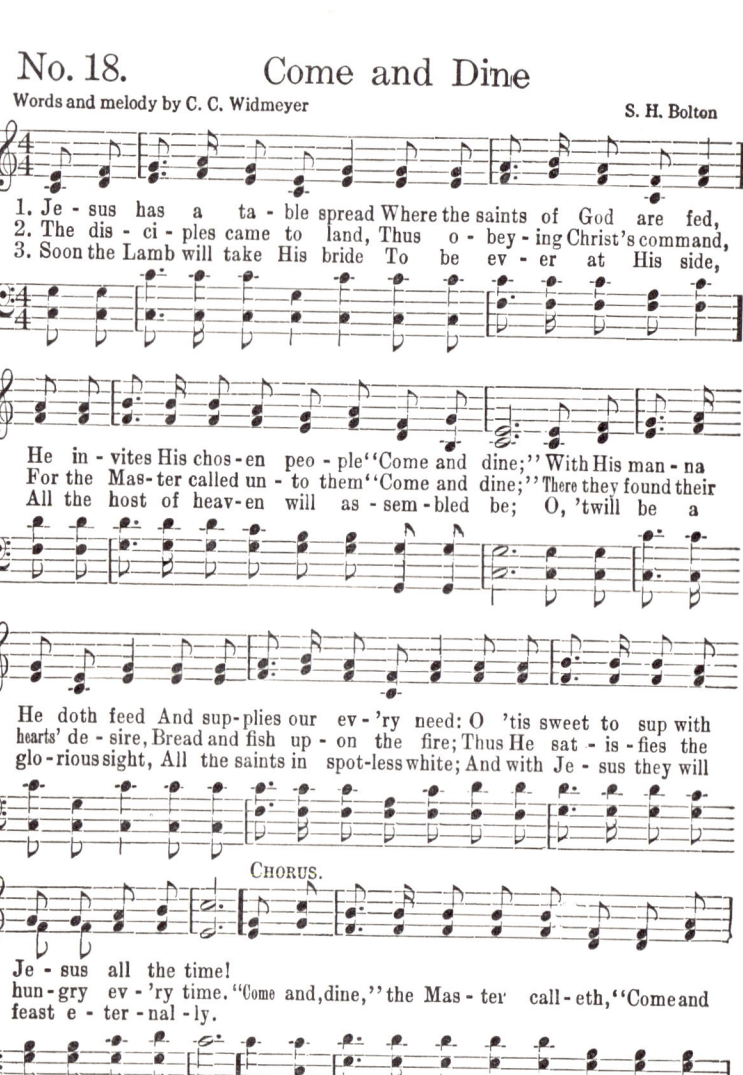

20. Tell It Wherever You Go.

Rev. Johnston Oatman, Jr.
Wm. Edie Marks.

1. If Christ the Re-deem-er has pardoned your sin, Tell it wher-ev-er you go;
2. If now you are happy with Christ as your Guide, Tell it wher-ev-er you go;
3. When troubles as-sail do you trust in Him still? Tell it wher-ev-er you go;
4. If you are an heir to a mansion on high, Tell it wher-ev-er you go;

If in-to your darkness His light has shown in, Tell it wher-ev-er you go.
If He is your Friend, and with Him you abide, Tell it wher-ev-er you go.
When sorrows o'erwhelm do you sink in His will? Tell it wher-ev-er you go.
Un-til you find rest in that home in the sky, Tell it wher-ev-er you go.

CHORUS.

Tell it,...... tell it,........ Tell it wher-ev-er you go; If
Tell it that others around you may know,

you would win oth-ers from sin and from woe, Tell it wher-ev-er you go!

Copyright Renewal, 1935, in "Full of Blessing No. 3" John T. Benson, Jr., Owner

No. 21 'Tis the Blessed Hour of Prayer.

Fanny J. Crosby.   COPYRIGHT, 1880, BY THE BIGLOW & MAIN CO. USED BY PER. OF W. H. DOANE.   W. H. Doane.

1. 'Tis the bless-ed hour of prayer, when our hearts low-ly bend, And we
2. 'Tis the bless-ed hour of prayer, when the Sav-ior draws near, With a
3. 'Tis the bless-ed hour of prayer, when the tempt-ed and tried To the
4. At the bless-ed hour of prayer, trust-ing Him, we be-lieve That the

gath-er to Je-sus, our Sav-ior and Friend; If we come to Him in
ten-der com-pas-sion His chil-dren to hear; When He tells us we may
Sav-ior who loves them their sor-row con-fide; With a sym-pa-thiz-ing
bless-ing we're need-ing we'll sure-ly re-ceive; In the full-ness of this

faith, His pro-tec-tion to share, What a balm for the wear-y!
cast at His feet ev-'ry care, What a balm for the wear-y!
heart He re-moves ev-'ry care; What a balm for the wear-y!
trust we shall lose ev-'ry care; What a balm for the wear-y!

D. S.—*What a balm for the wear-y!*

Fine. Chorus.   D. S.

O how sweet to be there! Bless-ed hour of prayer, bless-ed hour of prayer;

O how sweet to be there!

23. True-Hearted, Whole-Hearted

COPYRIGHT, 1916, BY GEO. C. STEBBINS. RENEWAL. HOPE PUBLISHING CO., OWNER
USED BY PERMISSION

FRANCES R. HAVERGAL
GEO. C. STEBBINS

1. True-hearted, whole-hearted, faithful and loyal, King of our lives, by Thy grace we will be; Under the standard exalted and royal, Strong in Thy strength we will battle for Thee.
2. True-hearted, whole-hearted, fullest allegiance Yielding henceforth to our glorious King; Valiant endeavor and loving obedience, Freely and joyously now would we bring.
3. True-hearted, whole-hearted, Savior all-glorious! Take Thy great power and reign there alone, Over our wills and affections victorious, Freely surrendered and wholly Thine own.

CHORUS

Peal out the watch-word! silence it never! Song of our spirits, rejoicing and free; Peal out the watch-word! loyal forever, King of our lives, by Thy grace we will be.

No. 26. The Last Mile of the Way.

Copyright Renewal, 1936, John T. Benson, Jr., Owner

Rev. Johnson Oatman, Jr.
Wm. Edie Marks.

1. If I walk in the path-way of du-ty, If I work till the close of the day;
2. If for Christ I proclaim the glad sto-ry, If I seek for His sheep gone a-stray,
3. Here the dearest of ties we must sev-er, Tears of sor-row are seen ev-'ry day;
4. And if here I have earn-est-ly striv-en, And have tried all His will to o-bey,

I shall see the great King in His beau-ty,
I am sure He will show me His glo-ry,
But no sickness, no sigh-ing for-ev-er
'Twill enhance all the rap-ture of heav-en,

Fine. Chorus.
When I've gone the last mile of the way. When I've gone the last mile of the way, I will rest at the close of the day, And I know there are joys that a-wait me,

D. S.—When I've gone the last mile of the way.

No. 32
BEAUTIFUL
Copyright, 1911, by J. A. Lee

B. E. W.
B. E. Warren

1. Beau-ti-ful robes so white, Beau-ti-ful land of light, Beau-ti-ful home so bright,
2. Beau-ti-ful tho't to me, We shall for-ev-er be Thine in e-ter-ni-ty,
3. Beau-ti-ful things on high, O-ver in yon-der sky, Thus I shall leave this shore,

Where there shall come no night; Beau-ti-ful crown I'll wear, Shining with stars o'er there,
When from this world we're free; Free from its toil and care, Heav-en-ly joys to share,
Count-ing my treasures o'er; Where we shall nev-er die, Car-ry me by and by,

CHORUS

Yon-der in mansions fair, Gather us there. Beau-ti-ful robes,....... Beau-ti-ful
Let me cross over there; This is my prayer.
Nev-er to sorrow more, Heavenly store. Beautiful robes of white,

land,......... Beau-ti-ful home,......... Beau-ti-ful band,..........
Beau-ti-ful land of light, Beau-ti-ful home so bright, Beau-ti-ful band of might,

Beau-ti-ful crown,............... Shin-ing so fair,..................
Beau-ti-ful, beau-ti-ful crown, Shin-ing, yes, shin-ing so fair,

One Day!

car-ried my sins far a-way; Ris-ing, He jus-ti-fied free-ly for-ev-er: One day He's com-ing—O glo-ri-ous day!

No. 35 'Tis so Sweet to Trust in Jesus.

MRS. LOUISA M. R. STEAD. WM. J. KIRKPATRICK.

1. 'Tis so sweet to trust in Je-sus, Just to take Him at His word; Just to rest up-on His promise; Just to know, "Thus saith the Lord."
2. O how sweet to trust in Je-sus, Just to trust His cleansing blood; Just in simple faith to plunge me 'Neath the healing, cleansing flood.
3. Yes, 'tis sweet to trust in Jesus, Just from sin and self to cease; Just from Jesus sim-ple tak-ing Life and rest, and joy and peace.
4. I'm so glad I learned to trust Thee, Precious Jesus, Saviour, Friend; And I know that Thou art with me, Wilt be with me to the end.

REFRAIN.

Je-sus, Je-sus, how I trust Him! How I've prov'd Him o'er and o'er! Jesus, Jesus, precious Jesus! O for grace to trust Him more.

No. 36 Though Your Sins Be As Scarlet.

Fanny J. Crosby.   COPYRIGHT, 1915, BY W. H. DOANE. RENEWAL. F. T. DOANE, OWNER.   W. H. Doane.

DUET. *Gently.*

1. "Tho' your sins be as scar-let, They shall be as white as snow; as snow;
2. Hear the voice that entreats you, O re-turn ye un-to God! to God!
3. He'll for-give your transgressions, And remember them no more; no more;

QUARTET.

Tho' they be red............ like crim-son, They shall be as wool;"
He is of great............ com-pas-sion, And of won-drous love;
"Look un-to Me,............ ye peo-ple," Saith the Lord your God;

(1) Tho' they be red

DUET. *p*   QUARTET. *f*

"Tho' your sins be as scar-let, Tho' your sins be as scar-let,
Hear the voice that en-treats you, Hear the voice that en-treats you,
He'll for-give your transgressions, He'll for-give your trans-gres-sions,

p rit.

They shall be as white as snow, They shall be as white as snow."
O re-turn ye un-to God! O re-turn ye un-to God!
And re-mem-ber them no more, And re-mem-ber them no more.

No. 37 We'll Understand It Better

C. A. T.
C. A. Tindley. Arr. by F. A. Clark.

1. We are oft-en toss'd and driv'n on the rest-less sea of time,
2. We are oft-en des-ti-tute of the things that life de-mands,
3. Tri-als dark on ev-'ry hand, and we can-not un-der-stand,
4. Temp-ta-tions, hid-den snares, oft-en take us un-a-wares,

Som-bre skies and howling tempests oft suc-ceed a bright sun-shine,
Want of food and want of shel-ter—thirst-y hills and bar-ren lands,
All the ways that God would lead us to that bless-ed Prom-ised Land;
And our hearts are made to bleed for many a thoughtless word or deed,

In that land of per-fect day, when the mists have roll'd a-way, We will
We are trust-ing in the Lord, and ac-cord-ing to his word, We will
But he guides us with his eye and we'll fol-low 'till we die, For we'll
And we won-der why the test when we try to do our best, But we'll

D.S.—how we've o-ver-come; For we'll

FINE. CHORUS.
un-der-stand it bet-ter by and by. (by and by.) By and by when the morning
un-der-stand it bet-ter by and by.

D.S.
comes, When the saints of God are gather'd home, We'll tell the sto-ry

No. 38 — DEEPER, DEEPER

Copyright, 1900, by C. P. Jones
Used by permission

C. P. J.   C. P. Jones

1. Deep-er, deep-er in the love of Je-sus Dai-ly let me go;
2. Deep-er, deep-er! bless-ed Ho-ly Spir-it, Take me deep-er still,
3. Deep-er, deep-er! tho' it cost hard tri-als, Deep-er let me go!
4. Deep-er, high-er, ev-'ry day in Je-sus, Till all con-flict past,

High-er, high-er in the school of wis-dom, More of grace to know.
Till my life is whol-ly lost in Je-sus, And His per-fect will.
Root-ed in the ho-ly love of Je-sus, Let me fruit-ful grow.
Finds me con-qu'ror, and in His own im-age Per-fect-ed at last.

CHORUS

O deep - - er yet, I pray, And
O deep-er yet, I pray, deep-er yet, I pray, And

high - er ev-'ry day, And wis - - er,
high-er ev-'ry day, high-er ev-'ry day, And wis-er, bless-ed Lord,

bless-ed Lord, In Thy pre-cious, ho-ly Word.
wis-er, bless-ed Lord,

No. 39 SOUND THE BATTLE CRY

W. F. S.
Wm. F. Sherwin

1. Sound the bat-tle cry! See, the foe is nigh; Raise the stand-ard high For the Lord; Gird your ar-mor on, Stand firm, ev-'ry one; Rest your cause up-on His ho-ly Word.

2. Strong to meet the foe, Marching on we go, While our cause, we know, Must pre-vail; Shield and banner bright, Gleam-ing in the light; Bat-tling for the right We ne'er can fail.

3. O Thou God of all, Hear us when we call, Help us one and all By Thy grace; When the bat-tle's done, And the vic-t'ry's won, May we wear the crown Be-fore Thy face.

Chorus. *ff*

Rouse, then, sol-diers, ral-ly round the ban-ner, Read-y, stead-y, pass the word a-long; On-ward, for-ward, shout a-loud Ho-san-na! Christ is Cap-tain of the might-y throng.

No. 40   HE ABIDES

Herbert Buffum.   Owned by God's Bible School   **D. M. Shanks.**

1. I'm re-joic-ing night and day, As I walk the pil-grim way, For the hand of God in all my life I see, And the rea-son of my bliss, Yes, the se-cret all is this: That the Com-fort-er a-bides with me.
2. Once my heart was full of sin, Once I had no peace with-in, Till I heard how Je-sus died up-on the tree; Then I fell down at His feet, And there came a peace so sweet, Now the Com-fort-er a-bides with me.
3. He is with me ev-'ry-where, And He knows my ev-'ry care, I'm as hap-py as a bird and just as free; For the spir-it has con-trol, Je-sus sat-is-fies my soul, Since the Com-fort-er a-bides with me!
4. There's no thirsting for the things Of the world—they've taken wings; Long a-go I gave them up, and in-stant-ly All my night was turned to day, All my bur-dens rolled a-way, Now the Com-fort-er a-bides with me!

CHORUS.

He a-bides, He a-bides, Hal-le-lu-jah, He a-bides with me! I'm re-joic-ing night and day, As I

HE ABIDES (Concluded)

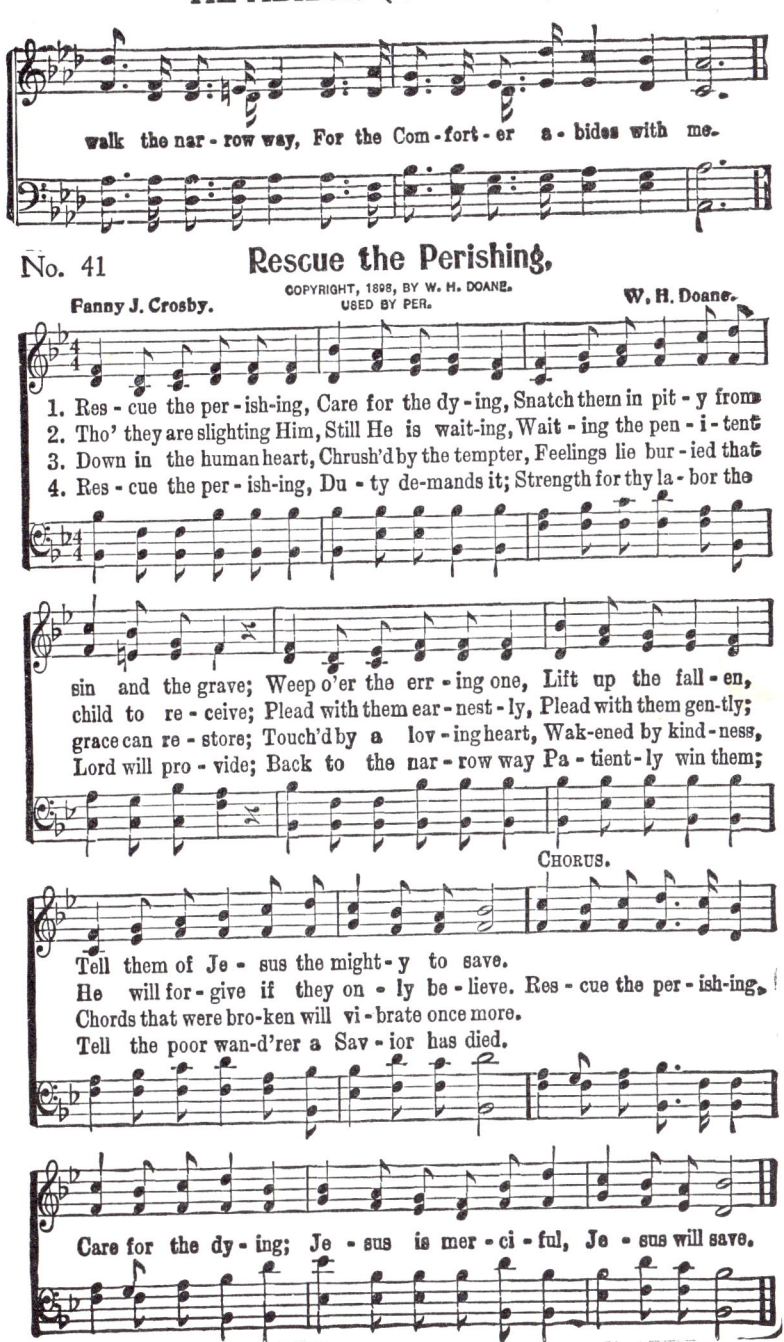

walk the nar - row way, For the Com - fort - er a - bides with me.

No. 41 **Rescue the Perishing.**

COPYRIGHT, 1898, BY W. H. DOANE.
USED BY PER.

Fanny J. Crosby. W. H. Doane.

1. Res - cue the per - ish - ing, Care for the dy - ing, Snatch them in pit - y from
2. Tho' they are slighting Him, Still He is wait - ing, Wait - ing the pen - i - tent
3. Down in the human heart, Chrush'd by the tempter, Feelings lie bur - ied that
4. Res - cue the per - ish - ing, Du - ty de - mands it; Strength for thy la - bor the

sin and the grave; Weep o'er the err - ing one, Lift up the fall - en,
child to re - ceive; Plead with them ear - nest - ly, Plead with them gen - tly;
grace can re - store; Touch'd by a lov - ing heart, Wak-ened by kind - ness,
Lord will pro - vide; Back to the nar - row way Pa - tient - ly win them;

CHORUS.

Tell them of Je - sus the might - y to save.
He will for - give if they on - ly be - lieve. Res - cue the per - ish - ing,
Chords that were bro - ken will vi - brate once more.
Tell the poor wan-d'rer a Sav - ior has died.

Care for the dy - ing; Je - sus is mer - ci - ful, Je - sus will save.

No. 42. If Jesus Goes With Me.

C. A. M.
C. Austin Miles.

1. It may be in the val-ley, where countless dan-gers hide; It may be in the sun-shine that I, in peace, a-bide; But this one thing I know— if it be dark or fair, If Je-sus is with me, I'll go a-ny-where!

2. It may be I must car-ry the bless-ed word of life A-cross the burning des-erts to those in sin-ful strife; And tho' it be my lot to bear my col-ors there, If Je-sus goes with me, I'll go a-ny-where!

3. But if it be my por-tion to bear my cross at home, While others bear their bur-dens be-yond the bil-low's foam, I'll prove my faith in him— con-fess his judgments fair, And, if he stays with me, I'll stay a-ny-where!

4. It is not mine to question the judgments of my Lord, It is but mine to fol-low the lead-ings of his Word; But if to go or stay, or whether here or there, I'll be, with my Sav-ior, con-tent a-ny-where!

Chorus.

If Je-sus goes with me, I'll go.... (I'll go) A-ny-where! 'Tis heaven to me, Wher-ev-er I may be, If he is there! I count it a priv-i-lege here... His (His cross, His)

Copyrighted 1936, renewal, The Rodeheaver Company, owner.

If Jesus Goes With Me. Concluded.

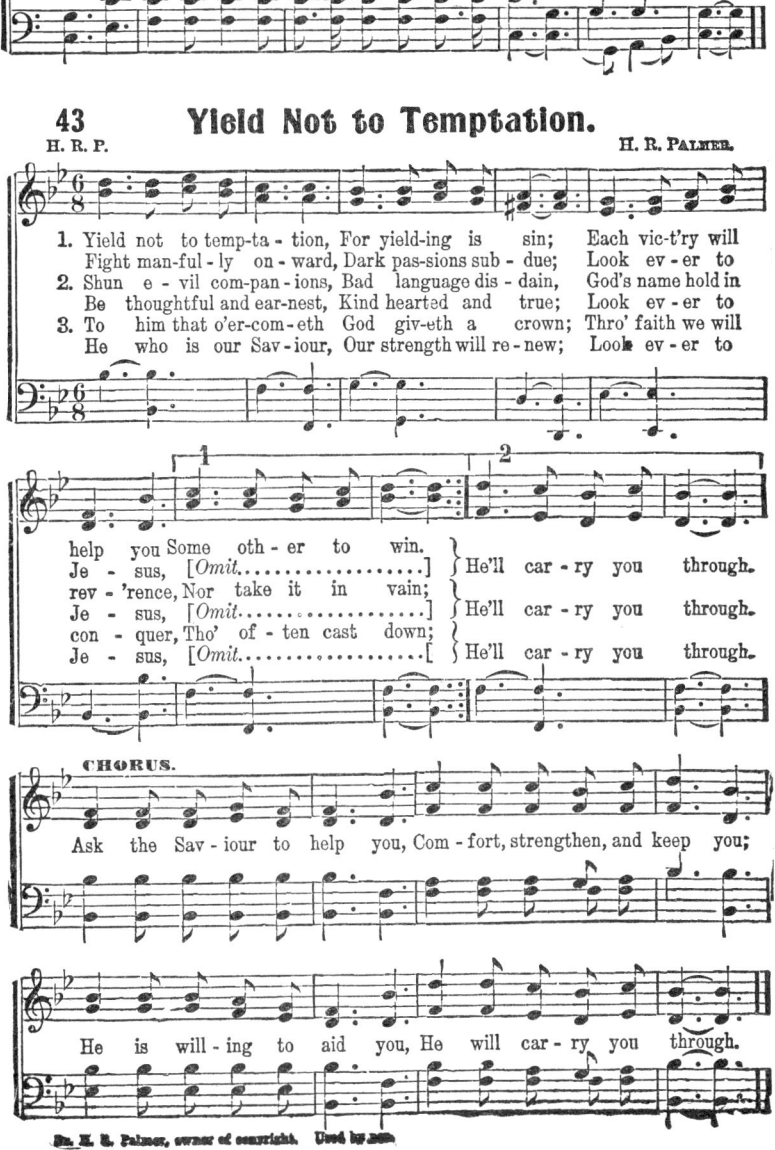

cross to bear;.... If Jesus goes with me, I'll go Anywhere!
cross, His cross to bear;

43   Yield Not to Temptation.

H. R. P.   H. R. PALMER.

1. Yield not to temp-ta-tion, For yield-ing is sin; Each vic-t'ry will
help you Some other to win.
Fight man-ful-ly on-ward, Dark pas-sions sub-due; Look ev-er to
Je - sus, [Omit................] }He'll car-ry you through.

2. Shun e-vil com-pan-ions, Bad language dis-dain, God's name hold in
rev-'rence, Nor take it in vain;
Be thoughtful and ear-nest, Kind hearted and true; Look ev-er to
Je - sus, [Omit................] }He'll car-ry you through.

3. To him that o'er-com-eth God giv-eth a crown; Thro' faith we will
con-quer, Tho' of-ten cast down;
He who is our Sav-iour, Our strength will re-new; Look ev-er to
Je - sus, [Omit................[}He'll car-ry you through.

CHORUS.

Ask the Sav-iour to help you, Com-fort, strengthen, and keep you;
He is will-ing to aid you, He will car-ry you through.

No. 44. THE NAME OF JESUS.

H. L. Copyright renewal, 1938, John T. Benson, Jr., owner. HALDOR LILLENAS.

1. There is a name of wondrous sweetness, Resplendent with immortal fame;
   I glory in its grand completeness; It is the Savior's precious name.
2. There is no name of rarer beauty; Then shall I ever blush with shame;
   Nay! 'tis my joy, and not a duty, To magnify my Savior's name.
3. There is no music like the story Of Jesus and His love divine;
   Illimitable in His glory, He reigns forever, He is mine.
4. This name, all other names transcending, Remains forevermore the same;
   Some day, with angel voices blending, I'll sing the praises of His name.

CHORUS.

Jesus, Jesus, Jesus took away my sin;
Jesus, precious, blessed Jesus, He took away my sin;
Jesus, Jesus, Jesus now abides within........
Jesus, precious, blessed Jesus, Yes, now abides within.
Then give me Jesus, Jesus, Now and evermore the same;......
Jesus, precious, blessed Jesus, forevermore;

THE NAME OF JESUS. Concluded.

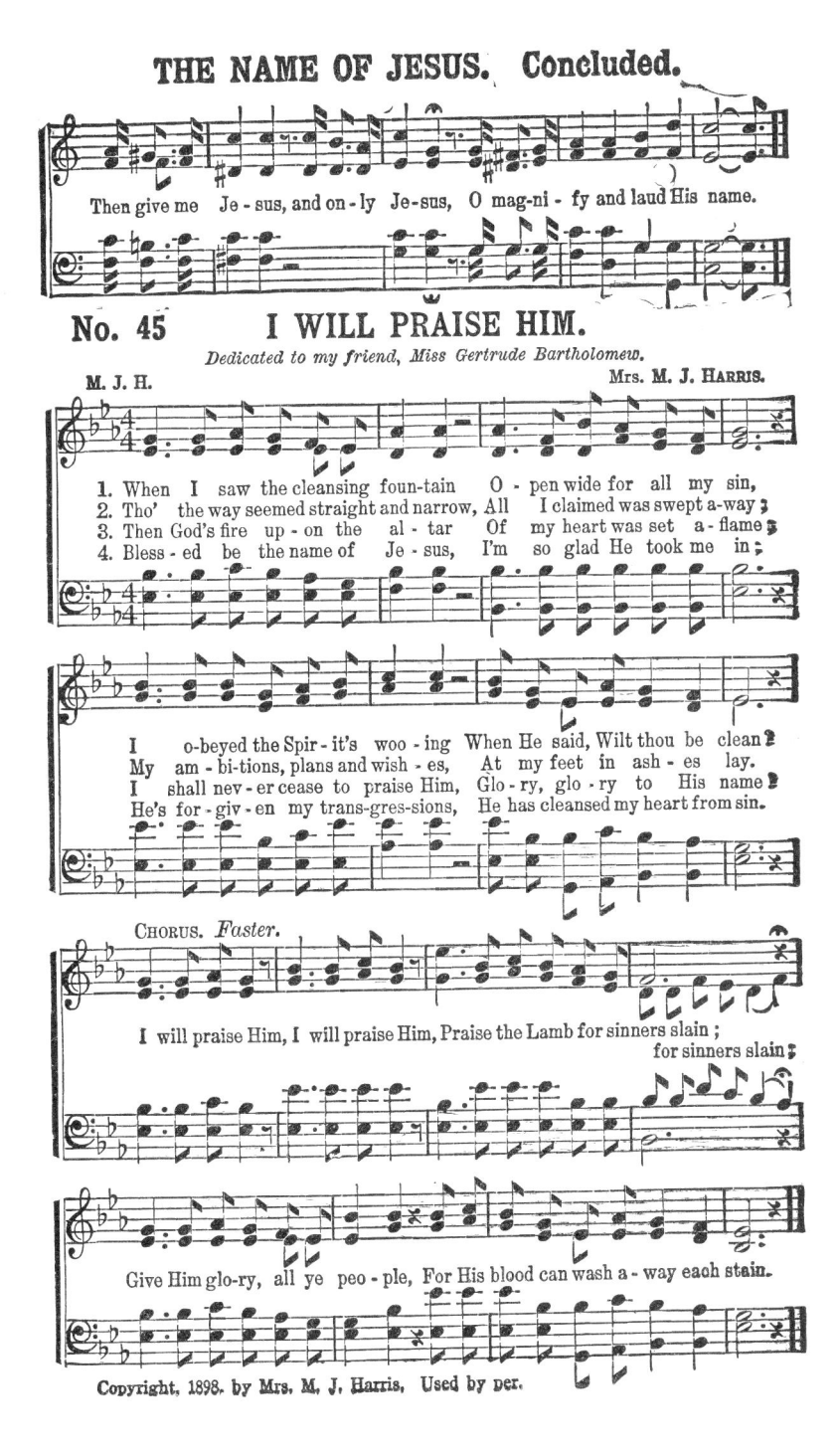

Then give me Je-sus, and on-ly Je-sus, O mag-ni-fy and laud His name.

No. 45. I WILL PRAISE HIM.

Dedicated to my friend, Miss Gertrude Bartholomew.

M. J. H. Mrs. M. J. HARRIS.

1. When I saw the cleansing foun-tain O-pen wide for all my sin,
2. Tho' the way seemed straight and narrow, All I claimed was swept a-way;
3. Then God's fire up-on the al-tar Of my heart was set a-flame;
4. Bless-ed be the name of Je-sus, I'm so glad He took me in;

I o-beyed the Spir-it's woo-ing When He said, Wilt thou be clean?
My am-bi-tions, plans and wish-es, At my feet in ash-es lay.
I shall nev-er cease to praise Him, Glo-ry, glo-ry to His name!
He's for-giv-en my trans-gres-sions, He has cleansed my heart from sin.

CHORUS. *Faster.*

I will praise Him, I will praise Him, Praise the Lamb for sinners slain;
for sinners slain;
Give Him glo-ry, all ye peo-ple, For His blood can wash a-way each stain.

Copyright, 1898, by Mrs. M. J. Harris. Used by per.

No. 46 OUR LORD'S RETURN TO EARTH AGAIN

J. M. K.   Acts 1: 9, 10, 11.   J. M. KIRK.

1. I am watch-ing for the com - ing of the glad mil - len - nial day,
2. Je - sus' com - ing back will be the an-swer to earth's sorrowing cry,
3. Yes, the ran-somed of the Lord shall come to Zi - on then with joy,
4. Then the sin and sor - row, pain and death of this dark world shall cease,

When our bless-ed Lord shall come and catch his wait - ing Bride a - way; Oh! my
For the knowledge of the Lord shall fill the earth and sea and sky; God shall
And in all His ho - ly mount-ain noth-ing hurts or shall de-stroy; Per-fect
In a glo-rious reign with Je - sus of a thousand years of peace; All the

heart is fill'd with rapture as I la-bor, watch and pray, For our Lord is com-ing
take a - way all sick-ness and the suff'rer's tears will dry, When our Saviour shall come
peace shall reign in ev-'ry heart, and love with-out al - loy, Aft - er Je-sus shall come
earth is groaning, cry-ing for that day of sweet release, For our Je - sus to come

D.S. *will be bound a thousand years, we'll have no tempter then, After Jesus shall come*

Fine. CHORUS.

back to earth a-gain. Oh! our Lord is coming back to earth a-gain,
                       is com-ing back to earth again,

back to earth a-gain.

D. S.

Yes, our Lord is com - ing back to earth a - gain,   Sa - tan
             is com - ing back to earth a - gain,

Copyright, 1894, by Myland & Kirk. Used by per.

47. It's So.

N. B. Herrell. N. B. Herrell.

1. Once I was blind to gos-pel light, My Lord I did not know;
2. My Sav-ior broke old Satan's chain, He had to let me go;
3. As I went on to sing and shout, I found an in-ward foe;
4. My heart is filled with per-fect love, I feel its ebb and flow;

But when I prayed he set me right, Praise the Lord, it's so.
For Christ came in my life to reign, Praise the Lord, it's so.
The Ho-ly Spir-it burned him out, Praise the Lord, it's so.
I'm hap-py on my way a-bove, Praise the Lord, it's so.

CHORUS.

Praise the Lord, it's so, Praise the Lord, it's so;
I know it's so, I know it's so;

Once I was blind, but now I see, Once I was bound, but now I'm free;

Thru Christ I shout the vic-to-ry. Praise the Lord, it's so.
it's so,

Copyrighted 1942, renewal, John T. Benson, Jr., owner.

No. 48 When Love Shines In.

Mrs. Frank A. Breck — Copyright, 1902, by Wm. J. Kirkpatrick — Wm. J. Kirkpatrick
Copyright Renewal, 1930—Hope Pub. Co., Owner

1. Jesus comes with pow'r to gladden, When love shines in, Ev-'ry life that woe can sad-den, When love shines in. Love will teach us how to pray, Love will drive the gloom away, Turn our darkness into day, When love shines in.
2. How the world will glow with beauty, When love shines in, And the heart re-joice in du-ty, When love shines in. Tri-als may be sanc-ti-fied, And the soul in peace a-bide, Life will all be glo-ri-fied, When love shines in.
3. Darkest sorrow will grow brighter, When love shines in, And the heav-iest bur-den light-er, When love shines in. 'Tis the glo-ry that will throw Light to show us where to go; O the heart shall blessing know When love shines in.
4. We may have un-fad-ing splendor, When love shines in, And a friend-ship true and ten-der, When love shines in. When earth-vict'ries shall be won, And our life in heav'n be-gun, There will be no need of sun, For love shines in.

CHORUS.

When love shines in,...... When love shines in,.... How the heart is tuned to singing, When love shines in;..... When love shines in,..... When
When love shines in, When love shines in, When love shines in,
When love shines in;... When love shines in;...
When love shines in, When love shines in

When Love Shines In. Concluded.

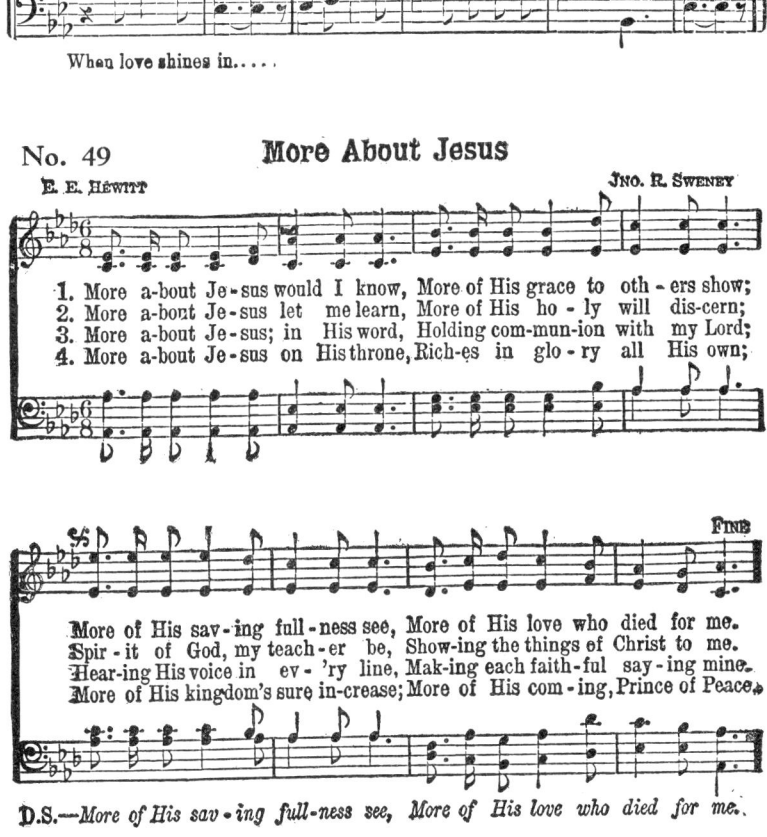

love shines in,.... Joy and peace to others bring, When love shines in.....
love, when love shines in.

When love shines in.....

No. 49 **More About Jesus**

E. E. Hewitt
Jno. R. Sweney

1. More a-bout Je-sus would I know, More of His grace to oth-ers show;
2. More a-bout Je-sus let me learn, More of His ho-ly will dis-cern;
3. More a-bout Je-sus; in His word, Holding com-mun-ion with my Lord;
4. More a-bout Je-sus on His throne, Rich-es in glo-ry all His own;

More of His sav-ing full-ness see, More of His love who died for me.
Spir-it of God, my teach-er be, Show-ing the things of Christ to me.
Hear-ing His voice in ev-'ry line, Mak-ing each faith-ful say-ing mine.
More of His kingdom's sure in-crease; More of His com-ing, Prince of Peace.

D.S.—More of His sav-ing full-ness see, More of His love who died for me.

REFRAIN   D.S.

More, more a-bout Je-sus, More, more a-bout Je-sus;

No. 50 In the Garden

C. A. M. Copyrighted 1940, renewal, The Rodeheaver Company, owner. C. Austin Miles.

1. I come to the gar-den a-lone, While the dew is still on the ros-es; And the voice I hear, Fall-ing on my ear, The Son of God dis-clos-es.

2. He speaks, and the sound of His voice Is so sweet the birds hush their sing-ing, And the mel-o-dy That He gave to me, With-in my heart is ring-ing.

3. I'd stay in the gar-den with Him Tho' the night a-round me be fall-ing, But He bids me go; Thro' the voice of woe His voice to me is call-ing.

CHORUS.

And He walks with me, and He talks with me, And He tells me I am His own, And the joy we share as we tar-ry there, None oth-er has ev-er known.

No. 51 **HEAVENLY SUNLIGHT**

"I am the Light of the world; he that followeth me shall not walk in the darkness."—John 8:12.

Rev. H. J. ZELLEY. G. H. COOK.

1. Walk-ing in sun-light, all of my jour-ney; O-ver the moun-tains thro' the deep vale; Je-sus has said I'll nev-er for-sake thee, Prom-ise di-vine that nev-er can fail.
2. Shad-ows a-round me, shad-ows a-bove me, Nev-er con-ceal my Sav-iour and Guide; He is the light, in Him is no dark-ness, Ev-er I'm walk-ing close to His side.
3. In the bright sun-light, ev-er re-joic-ing, Press-ing my way to man-sions a-bove; Sing-ing His prais-es glad-ly I'm walk-ing, Walk-ing in sun-light, sun-light of love.

CHORUS.

Heav-en-ly sun-light, heav-en-ly sun-light; Flooding my soul with glo-ry di-vine: Hal-le-lu-jah, I am re-joic-ing, Sing-ing His prais-es, Je-sus is mine.

No. 52 — HE BROUGHT ME OUT

"He hath put a new song in my mouth, even praise unto our God"—Ps. 40: 1-3.

REV. H. J. ZELLEY. Cho. by H. L. G. H. L. GILMOUR.

1. My heart was dis-tressed 'neath Je-ho-vah's dread frown, And low in the pit where my sins dragg'd me down; I cried to the Lord from the deep, mir-y clay, Who ten-der-ly bro't me out to gold-en day.

2. He placed me up-on the strong rock by His side, My steps were es-tab-lished and here I'll a-bide; No dan-ger of fall-ing while here I re-main, But stand by His grace un-til the crown I gain.

3. He gave me a song, 'twas a new song of praise, By day and by night its sweet notes I will raise; My heart's o-ver-flow-ing, I'm hap-py and free, I'll praise my Re-deem-er, who has res-cued me.

4. I'll sing of His won-der-ful mer-cy to me, I'll praise Him till all men His good-ness shall see; I'll sing of sal-va-tion at home and a-broad, Till ma-ny shall hear the truth and trust in God.

5. I'll tell of the pit, with its gloom and de-spair, I'll praise the dear Fa-ther, who an-swered my pray'r; I'll sing my new song, the glad sto-ry of love, Then join in the cho-rus with the saints a-bove.

CHORUS.

He bro't me out of the mir-y clay, He set my feet on the rock to stay; He puts a song in my soul to-day, A song of praise, hal-le-lu-lah.

No. 53 REDEEMED

Fanny M. Crosby
Copyright, 1882; 1910 Renewal, by Wm. J. Kirkpatrick.
Wm. J. Kirkpatrick

1. Redeemed, how I love to pro-claim it! Redeemed by the blood of the Lamb;
2. Redeemed and so hap-py in Je-sus, No language my rapture can tell;
3. I think of my blessed Re-deem-er, I think of Him all the day long;
4. I know I shall see in His beau-ty, The King in whose law I de-light;
5. I know there's a crown that is waiting, In yonder bright mansion for me;

Redeemed thro' His in-fi-nite mer-cy, His child, and for-ev-er, I am.
I know that the light of His presence With me doth contin-ual-ly dwell.
I sing, for I can-not be si-lent, His love is the theme of my song.
Who lov-ing-ly guardeth my footsteps, And giveth me songs in the night.
And soon with the spir-its made perfect, At home with the Lord I shall be.

Chorus

Redeemed, Redeemed, Redeemed by the blood of the Lamb;
Redeemed, Redeemed,

Redeemed, Redeemed, His child, and for-ev-er, I am.
Redeemed, Redeemed,

No. 54 SAVED TO THE UTTERMOST

W. J. K.
WM. J. KIRKPATRICK. By per.

1. Saved to the ut-ter-most: I am the Lord's; Je-sus my
2. Saved to the ut-ter-most: Je-sus is near; Keep-ing me
3. Saved to the ut-ter-most: this I can say, "Once all was
4. Saved to the ut-ter-most: cheer-ful-ly sing Loud hal-le-

Sav-ior, sal-va-tion af-fords; Gives me his Spir-it a
safe-ly, He cast-eth out fear; Trust-ing His prom-is-es,
dark-ness, but now it is day; Beau-ti-ful vis-ions of
lu-ias to Je-sus, my King! Ransomed and pardoned, re-

wit-ness with-in, Whisp'ring of par-don, and sav-ing from sin.
how I am blest; Lean-ing up-on Him, how sweet is my rest.
glo-ry I see, Je-sus in brightness revealed un-to me."
deemed by His blood, Cleansed from unrighteousness, glo-ry to God.

REFRAIN.

Saved, saved, saved to the ut-ter-most, Saved, saved by pow-er di-vine;

Saved, saved, I'm saved to the ut-ter-most; Je-sus, the Savior, is mine.

No. 55 He's a Wonderful Savior to Me.

Virgil P. Brock. COPYRIGHT, 1918, BY HOMER A. RODEHEAVER. Blanche Kerr Brock
INTERNATIONAL COPYRIGHT SECURED.

1. I was lost in sin but Je-sus rescued me, He's a won-der-ful Savior to me; I was bound by fear but Je-sus set me free, He's a won-der-ful Sav-ior to me.
2. He's a Friend so true, so pa-tient and so kind, He's a won-der-ful Savior to me; Ev-'ry-thing I need in Him I al-ways find, He's a won-der-ful Sav-ior to me.
3. He is al-ways near to com-fort and to cheer, He's a won-der-ful Savior to me; He for-gives my sins. He dries my ev-'ry tear, He's a won-der-ful Sav-ior to me.
4. Dear-er grows the love of Je-sus day by day, He's a won-der-ful Savior to me; Sweeter is His grace while press-ing on my way, He's a won-der-ful Sav-ior to me.

CHORUS.

So won-der-ful! For He's a won-der-ful Sav-ior to me, He's a won-der-ful Sav-ior to me; I was lost in sin, but Je-sus took me in, He's a won-der-ful Sav-ior to me.

No. 56 — IT IS MINE

Elisha A. Hoffman.
Wm. Edie Marks.

1. God's a-bid-ing peace is in my soul to-day, Yes, I feel it now, yes, I feel it now; He has ta-ken all my doubts and fears a-way, Tho' I can-not tell you how.
2. He has wrought in me a sweet and per-fect rest, In my rap-tured heart I can feel it now; He each pass-ing mo-ment keeps me saved and blest, Floods with light my heart and brow.
3. He has giv-en me a nev-er-fail-ing joy, Oh, I have it now, oh, I have it now! To His praise I will my ransomed pow'rs em-ploy, And re-new my grate-ful vow.
4. Oh, the love of God is com-fort-ing my soul, For His love is mine, yes, His love is mine! Waves of joy and glad-ness o'er my spir-it roll, Thrill-ing me with life di-vine.

CHORUS.

It is mine, mine, It is mine, this priceless treasure, ev-er bless-ed be His name! He has giv-en peace, perfect peace to me; It is

COPYRIGHT, 1902, BY HENRY DATE. USED BY PER.

IT IS MINE (Concluded)

mine, mine, bless-ed be His name! Mine for all e-ter-ni-ty.
mine, this precious treasure, ev-er,

No. 57 OLD TIME POWER

"They were all filled with the Holy Ghost."—ACTS 2:4.

C. D. T.
Copyright, 1895, by Charlie D. Tillman. Charlie D. Tillman.

1. They were in the up-per cham-ber, They were all with one ac-cord,
2. Yes, this pow'r from heav'n de-scend-ed, With the sound of rush-ing wind;
3. Yes, this "old time" pow'r was giv-en To our fa-thers who were true;

When the Ho-ly Ghost de-scend-ed, As was prom-ised by our Lord.
Tongues of fire came down up-on them, As the Lord said He would send.
This is prom-ised to be-liev-ers, And we all may have it, too.

CHORUS.

O Lord, send the pow'r just now; O Lord, send the pow'r just now;

O Lord, send the pow'r just now, And bap-tize ev-'ry one.

No. 58. NEVER KNOWN TO FAIL.

ALICE JEAN CLEATOR.   HERBERT J. LACEY.

1. O the prom-is-es of God Long have Sa-tan's might withstood, And no pow'r of darkness o'er them shall pre-vail; They are build-ed sure and strong For the con-flict with the wrong, And those prom-is-es were nev-er known to fail!

2. O the might-y hand of time Fash-ions many a work sublime, Yet the tide of years their splendor shall as-sail; But the Word of God, this hour, Thrills with all the old-time pow'r, For those prom-is-es were nev-er known to fail!

3. Trust those ho-ly words to-day, Let them guide you on life's way, Seek their ref-uge in temp-ta-tion's rough-est gale; Strength and courage they shall lend, Pow'r from heav-en shall de-scend, For those prom-is-es were nev-er known to fail!

CHORUS.

God's prom-is-es were nev-er known to fail! were nev-er known to fail! No pow'r of darkness o'er them shall prevail! shall prevail! They are builded sure and strong

Copyright Renewal, 1932, the Rodeheaver Co., Owner

NEVER KNOWN TO FAIL. Concluded.

For the con-flict with the wrong, God's prom-is-es were nev-er known to fail!

No. 59 MARCHING ON THE KING'S HIGHWAY.

Rev. T. C. Harper. J. Owen Long.

1. Come and join the roy-al ar - my Marching on the King's high-way;
2. Press-ing onward, ev-er faith - ful, Rest-ing nev-er by the way;
3. Lift-ing up the faint and fall - en, Bear-ing bur-dens by the way;
4. Soon the jour-ney will be o - ver, Soon we'll lay our bur-dens down;

Gath'ring vol-un-teers for Je - sus As we're marching day by day.
Look-ing for the heav'nly cit - y Where the man-y loved ones stay.
Ev - er in the thick-est con - flict, Shirk-ing not the dread-ful fray.
En - ter thro' the o - pen por - tals; There re-ceive a harp and crown.

Chorus.

Marching, marching, Soldiers brave and true; Hear our happy song, As we march a-long;

Hap-py, hap-py, Hap-py all the day, March-ing on the King's high-way.

Copyright, 1908, by John T. Benson, Nashville, Tenn.

No. 60 — WHEN I SEE THE BLOOD.

JOHN.   J. G. F.

1. Christ our Re-deem-er died on the cross, Died for the sin-ner, paid all his due; All who re-cieve Him need nev-er fear,
2. Chief-est of sin-ners, Je-sus can save, As He has promised, so will He do; Oh, sin-ner, hear Him, trust in His word,
3. Judg-ment is com-ing, all will be there, Who have re-ject-ed, who have re-fused? Oh, sin-ner, hast-en, let Je-sus in,
4. O, what com-pas-sion, oh, boundless love! Je-sus hath pow-er, Je-sus is true; All who be-lieve are safe from the storm,

CHORUS

Yes, He will pass, will pass o-ver you.
Then He will pass, will pass o-ver you. When I see the blood,
Then God will pass, will pass o-ver you.
Oh, He will pass, will pass o-ver you.

When I see the blood, When I see the blood, When I see the blood, I will pass, I will pass o-ver you.

By Foote Bros., not copyrighted. Let no one do so. May this song ever be free to be published for the glory of God.

61. I'll Live On

T. J. L.
Used by permission
Thos. J. Laney

1. 'Tis a sweet and glorious tho't that comes to me, I'll live on,
2. When my bod-y's slumb'ring in the cold, cold clay,
3. When the world's on fire and dark-ness veils the sun,
4. In the glo-ry-land, with Je-sus on the throne,

I'll live on, yes, I'll live on; Je-sus saved my soul from death and now I'm free,
yes, I'll live on; There to sleep in Je-sus till the judg-ment day,
yes, I'll live on; Men will cry and to the rocks and moun-tains run,
yes, I'll live on; Thru e-ter-nal a-ges sing-ing, home, sweet home,

Chorus

I'll live on, yes, I'll live on. I'll live on, yes, I'll live
I'll live on, and on,

on, Thru e-ter-ni-ty I'll live on, I'll live on,
and on, and on,

yes, I'll live on, Thru e-ter-ni-ty I'll live on.
and on, yes, I'll live on.

No. 62 — MY BURDENS ROLLED AWAY

M. A. S.
Mrs. Minnie A. Steele

1. I remember when my burdens rolled away, I had carried them for years, night and day; When I sought the blessed Lord, and I took Him at His word,
2. I remember where my burdens rolled away, That I feared would never leave, night or day; Jesus showed to me the loss, so I left them at the cross,
3. I remember why my burdens rolled away, That had hindered me for years, night and day; As I sought the throne of grace, just a glimpse of Jesus' face,
4. I am singing since my burdens rolled away, There's a song within my heart, night and day; I am living for my King, and with joy I shout and sing,

CHORUS.

Then at once all my burdens rolled away.
I was glad when my burdens rolled away.
And I knew that my burdens could not stay.
Hallelujah! all my burdens rolled away.

Rolled away, rolled away, rolled away, I am happy since my burdens rolled away; Rolled away, rolled away, rolled away, I am happy since my burdens rolled away.

Copyright, 1907, by I. G. Martin, Mansfield, Ill. Used by per.

No. 63. A Soul Winner for Jesus.

"The law of the Lord is perfect, converting the soul."—Ps. 19: 7.

Copyright, 1935, Renewal, (By J. E. Thomas and J. W. Ferrill).

W. FERRILL.   J. W. FERRILL.

1. I want to be a soul winner For Je-sus ev-'ry day, He does so much for me;
2. I want to be a soul winner And bring the lost to Christ, That they His grace may know;
3. I want to be a soul winner Till Jesus calls for me, To lay my burdens down;

I want to aid the lost sinner To leave his erring way, And be from bondage free.
I want to live for Christ ever, And do His blessed will, Be-cause He loves me so.
I want to hear Him say, servant, "You've gathered many sheaves, Receive a starry crown."

CHORUS.

A soul......... winner for Je-sus, A soul......... winner for
A soul win-ner for Je-sus   Christ the Lord, A soul winner for Je-sus

Je - sus, O let me be each day A soul......... win-ner for
Christ the Lord, O let me be each day A soul winner for Je - sus

Je - sus, A soul...... winner for Je - sus, He's done so much for me.
Christ the Lord, A soul winner for Jesus Christ the Lord,

No. 64 — Constantly Abiding.

Mrs. W. L. M. — Mrs. Will L. Murphy.

1. There's a peace in my heart, that the world nev-er gave, A peace it can not take a-way; Tho' the tri-als of life may sur-round like a cloud, I've a peace that has come there to stay!
2. All the world seemed to sing of a Sav-iour and King, When peace sweetly came to my heart; Trou-bles all fled a-way and my night turned to day, Bless-ed Je-sus, how glorious Thou art!
3. This treas-ure I have in a tem-ple of clay, While here on His foot-stool I roam; But He's com-ing to take me some glo-ri-ous day, O-ver there to my heav-en-ly home!

CHORUS.

Con-stant-ly a-bid-ing, Je-sus is mine;
Con-stant-ly a-bid-ing, Je-sus is mine, yes, Je-sus is mine;
Con-stant-ly a-bid-ing, rap-ture di-
Con-stant-ly a-bid-ing, con-stant-ly a-bid-ing, rap-ture di-vine, O

Copyright 1936, Renewal, by Nazarene Publishing House.

Constantly Abiding. Concluded.

vine; He nev-er leaves me lone - - ly, whispers,
rap-ture di-vine: He nev-er leaves me, nev-er leaves me lonely, whispers,

O so kind:— "I will nev-er leave Thee," Je - sus is mine.
whispers, O so kind:— never leave Thee," Jesus, Je-sus is mine.

No. 65 **Home of the Soul.**

MRS. ELLEN H. GATES. PHILIP PHILLIPS.

1. I will sing you a song of that beau-ti-ful land, The far - a-way home
2. Oh, that home of the soul, in my visions and dreams Its bright jas-per walls
3. That unchangeable home is for you and for me, Where Je-sus of Naz-
4. Oh, how sweet it will be in that beau-ti-ful land, So free from all sor-

of the soul; Where no storms ever beat on the glittering strand, While the years
I can see; Till I fan-cy but thin-ly the veil intervenes Be-tween
a-reth stands; The King of all kingdoms for-ev-er is He; And He hold-
row and pain, With songs on our lips and with harps in our hands To meet

of e-ter-ni-ty roll, While the years of e-ter-ni-ty roll; ty roll.
the fair cit-y and me, Be - tween the fair cit-y and me; and me.
eth our crowns in His hands, And He holdeth our crowns in His hands; His hands.
one an-oth-er a-gain, To meet one an-oth-er a-gain; a-gain.

No. 66 — It Is Truly Wonderful

B. E. W.
Copyright, 1897, by Charlie D. Tillman.
B. E. Warren.

1. He par-doned my trans-gres-sions, He sanc-ti-fied my soul,
2. He keeps me ev-'ry mo-ment By trust-ing in His grace;
3. He brings me thro' af-flic-tion, He leaves me not a-lone;
4. He pros-pers and pro-tects me, His bless-ings ev-er flow;
5. He keeps me firm and faith-ful, His love I do en-joy,
6. There's not a sin-gle bless-ing Which we re-ceive on earth

He hon-ors my con-fes-sions, Since by His blood I'm whole.
'Tis thro' His blest at-tone-ment, That I may see His face.
He's with me in temp-ta-tion, He keeps me for His own.
He fills me with His glo-ry, He makes me white as snow.
For this I shall be grate-ful, And live in His em-ploy.
That does not come from heav-en, The source of our new birth.

CHORUS.

It is tru-ly won-der-ful What the Lord has done! It is tru-ly won-der-ful! It is tru-ly won-der-ful! It is tru-ly won-der-ful What the Lord has done! Glo-ry to His name.

No. 67 THE LILY OF THE VALLEY
J. R. Murray   Arr. by Thoro Harris

1. I've found a friend in Jesus, He's ev-'ry-thing to me, He's the fairest of ten
2. He all my griefs has tak-en, and all my sorrows borne; In temp-ta-tion He's my
3. He'll nev-er, nev-er leave me, nor yet forsake me here, While I live by faith and

thousand to my soul; The Lil-y of the Val-ley in Him a-lone I see, All I
strong and mighty tow'r; I've all for Him forsaken, I've all my idols torn From my
do His bless-ed will; A wall of fire about me, I've nothing now to fear; With His

need to cleanse and make me fully whole. In sorrow He's my comfort, in trouble He's my
heart, and now He keeps me by His pow'r. Tho' all the world forsake me, and Satan tempts me
manna He my hungry soul shall fill; Then sweeping up to glory, we'll see His blessed

CHORUS.—*In sorrow He's my comfort, in trouble He's my*

stay, He tells me ev-'ry care on Him to roll. Hallelujah! He's the Lil-y of the
sore, Thru Je-sus I shall safely reach the goal.   He's the Lil-y of the
face, Where rivers of delight shall ev - er roll.   He's the Lil-y of the

stay; He tells me ev-'ry care on Him to roll. (Hallelujah!) He's the Lil-y of the

D. S

Valley, the bright and morning Star, He's the fairest of ten thousand to my soul.

Valley, the bright and morning Star, He's the fairest of ten thousand to my soul.

No. 68 Saved.

J. P. S. Copyright Renewal, 1939—Robert Coleman, Owner J. P. SCHOLFIELD

1. I've found a friend who is all to me,.... His love is ev-er true;............ I love to tell how He lift-ed me,.... And what His grace can do for you....
2. He saves me from ev-'ry sin and harm... Se-cures my soul each day;............ I'm lean-ing strong on His might-y arm;... I know He'll guide me all the way....
3. When poor and need-y and all a-lone,... In love He said to me,............ Come un-to me and I'll lead you home,. To live with me e-ter-nal-ly."....

CHORUS.

Saved..... by His pow'r divine, Saved...... to new life sublime!
Saved by His pow'r,   Saved to new life,

cres. *rit.*
Life now is sweet and my joy is complete, for I'm saved, saved, saved!

No. 69   WHERE HE LEADS I'LL FOLLOW

Copyright, 1885, by W. A. Ogden

W. A. O.   W. A. Ogden

1. Sweet are the prom-is-es, Kind is the word; Dear-er far than an-y mes-sage man ev-er heard; Pure was the mind of Christ, Sin-less, I see; He the great ex-am-ple is, and pat-tern for me.

2. Sweet is the ten-der love Je-sus hath shown, Sweet-er far than an-y love that mor-tals have known; Kind to the err-ing one, Faith-ful is He; He the great ex-am-ple is, and pat-tern for me.

3. List to His lov-ing words, "Come un-to me!" Wear-y, heav-y-lad-en, there is sweet rest for thee; Trust in His prom-is-es, Faith-ful and sure; Lean up-on the Sav-ior, and thy soul is se-cure.

CHORUS.

Where . . . . He leads I'll fol - - - low,
Where He leads I'll fol-low, Where He leads I'll fol-low,
Fol - - low all the way; Follow Jesus ev-'ry day.
Fol-low all the way. yes, fol-low all the way;

No. 70   **Some Bright Morning**

Charlotte G. Homer / Chas. H. Gabriel

1. Be not a-wea-ry, for la-bor will cease,
2. Wea-ri-some bur-dens will all be laid down, Some glad morn-ing;
3. La-bor well done shall re-ceive its re-ward,
4. Oh, what a time of re-joic-ing will come,

Tur-moil will chang in-to in-fi-nite peace
Then shall our cross be ex-changed for a crown, Some bright morn-ing.
Thou who art faith-ful shalt be with the Lord,
When all the ran-somed are gathered at home,

CHORUS

Some bright morn-ing. Some glad morn-ing, When the sun is shin-ing in th' e-ter-nal sky;...... Some bright morn-ing, Some glad morn-ing We shall see the Lord of Har-vest by and by.

Copyrighted 1926, The Rodeheaver Company, owner.

No. 71   **I am Thine, O Lord.**

F. J. Crosby.   W. H. Doane.
COPYRIGHT, 1903, BY W. H. DOANE. RENEWAL.
USED BY PERMISSION.

1. I am Thine, O Lord, I have heard Thy voice, And it told Thy love to me;
2. Con-se-crate me now to Thy service, Lord, By the pow'r of grace di-vine;
3. O the pure de-light of a sin-gle hour That before Thy throne I spend,
4. There are depths of love that I can-not know Till I cross the nar-row sea;

But I long to rise in the arms of faith, And be clo-ser drawn to Thee.
Let my soul look up with a stead-fast hope, And my will be lost in Thine.
When I kneel in pray'r, and with Thee, my God, I commune as friend with friend!
There are heights of joy that I may not reach Till I rest in peace with Thee.

REFRAIN.

Draw me near - er, nearer, blessed Lord, To the cross where Thou hast died;
near-er, near-er,

Draw me nearer, nearer, nearer, blessed Lord, To Thy precious, bleeding side.

No. 72
C. P. J.

COME UNTO ME

Charles P. Jones

1. Hear the blessed Saviour calling the oppressed, "O ye heavy-laden, come to Me and rest;
2. Are you disappointed, wand'ring here and there, Dragging chains of doubt and loaded down with care?
3. Stumbling on the mountains dark with sin and shame, Stumbling tow'rd the pit of hell's consuming flame,
4. Have you cares of business, cares of pressing debt? Cares of social life or cares of hopes unmet?
6. Have you by temptation often conquered been, Has a sense of weakness brought distress within?

Come, no longer tar-ry, I your load will bear, Bring Me ev'ry burden, bring Me ev'ry care."
Do un-ho-ly feelings struggle in your breast? Bring your case to Jesus, He will give you rest.
By the pow'rs of sin deluded and oppressed, Hear the tender Shepherd,—"Come to Me and rest."
Are you by remorse or sense of guilt depressed? Come right on to Jesus, He will give you rest.
Christ will sanctify you, if you'll claim His best, In the Ho-ly Spir-it He will give you rest.

CHORUS.

Come un-to Me; I........ will give you
Come un-to Me, Come un-to Me, I will give you rest,

rest; Take........ My yoke up-on you,
I will give you rest; Take My yoke up-on you, Take My yoke up-on you,

Hear........ Me and be blest;........ I........ am
Hear Me and be blest, hear Me and be blest, I am meek and low-

COME UNTO ME—Concluded

meek and low - ly, Come........ and trust my might;
ly; I am meek and lowly, Come and trust my might, Come and trust my might,

Come, my yoke is eas - y, And.... my burden's light.
Come, O come, Come, my yoke is easy, Come, O come, Come, my burden's light.

No. 73 Let the Lower Lights be Burning.

P. P. B.   MATT. 5: 16.   P. P. BLISS.

1. Brightly beams our Father's mercy, From His light-house evermore,
2. Dark the night of sin has set-tled, Loud the an-gry billows roar;
3. Trim your feeble lamp, my brother: Some poor sailor tempest-tost,

But to us He gives the keeping Of the lights a-long the shore.
Ea-ger eyes are watching, longing, For the lights a-long the shore.
Try-ing now to make the harbor, In the darkness may be lost.

D.S.—*Some poor fainting, struggling seaman You may res-cue, you may save.*

CHORUS.
Let the low-er lights be burning! Send a gleam a-cross the wave!

No. 74   There is Glory in My Soul!

Grace Weiser Davis.   Chas. H. Gabriel.

1. Since I lost my sins and I found my Sav-ior, There is glo-ry in my soul! Since by faith I sought and ob-tained God's fa-vor, There is glo-ry in my soul!
2. Since He cleansed my heart, gave me sight for blind-ness, There is glo-ry in my soul! Since He touched and healed me in lov-ing kind-ness, There is glo-ry in my soul!
3. Since with God I've walked, hav-ing sweet com-mun-ion, There is glo-ry in my soul! Bright-er grows each day in this heav'n-ly un-ion, There is glo-ry in my soul!
4. Since I en-tered Canaan on my way to heav-en, There is glo-ry in my soul! Since the day my life to the Lord was giv-en, There is glo-ry in my soul!

CHORUS.

There is glo-ry, glo-ry, there is glo-ry in my soul! Ev-'ry day brighter grows, And I con-quer all my foes; There is glo-ry, glo-ry, there is glo-ry in my soul! There is glo-ry in my soul!

Copyrighted 1922, Renewal, The Rodeheaver Company, Owner.

75. Lead Me Gently Home

Will L. Thompson and Co., owner of copyright

W. L. T.
W. L. Thompson

SOLO or DUET. *ad lib.*

1. Lead me gen-tly home, Fa-ther, Lead me gen-tly home, When life's toils are end-ed, And part-ing days have come; Sin no more shall tempt me, Ne'er from Thee I'll roam, If Thou'lt on-ly lead me, Fa-ther, Lead me gen-tly home.

2. Lead me gen-tly home, Fa-ther, Lead me gen-tly home, In life's dark-est hours, Father, When life's troubles come, Keep my feet from wand'ring, Lest from Thee I roam, Lest I fall up-on the way-side, Lead me gen-tly home.

REFRAIN.

Lead me gen-tly home, Fa-ther, Lead me gen-tly, Lead me gen-tly home, Fa-ther, Lead me gen-tly home, Fa-ther, Lest I fall up-on the way-side, Lead me gen-tly home.

No. 76   He Ransomed Me

Julia H. Johnston   J. W. Henderson

1. There's a sweet and bless-ed sto-ry Of the Christ who came from glo-ry,
2. From the depth of sin and sad-ness To the heights of joy and glad-ness
3. From the throne of heav'nly glo-ry—Oh, the sweet and bless-ed sto-ry!
4. By and by with joy in-creas-ing, And with grat-i-tude un-ceas-ing

Just to res-cue me from sin and mis-er-y; He in lov-ing kind-ness sought me
Je-sus lift-ed me, in mer-cy full and free; With His precious blood He bo't me
Je-sus came to lift the lost in sin and woe In-to lib-er-ty all-glo-rious
Lift-ed up with Christ for-ev-er-more to be; I will join the hosts there sing-ing,

ad lib.

And from sin and shame hath bro't me, Hal-le-lu-jah! Je-sus ran-somed me.
When I knew Him not, He sought me, And in love di-vine He ransomed me.
Tro-phies of His grace vic-to-rious, Ev-er-more re-joic-ing here be-low.
In the an-them ev-er ring-ing, To the King of Love who ransomed me.

Chorus

Hal-le-lu-jah, what a Sav-ior! Who can take a poor lost sin-ner, Lift Him from the mi-ry clay and set Him free; (Hal-le-lu-jah) I will ev-er tell the sto-ry

Copyright Renewal 1944—John T. Benson, Jr., owner

He Ransomed Me

Shout-ing glo-ry, glo-ry, glo-ry, Hal-le-lu-jah! Je-sus ran-somed me.

No. 77 Some Glad Day When Jesus Comes

F. M. L. FRANK M. LYNN, OWNER, 1920 Frank M. Lynn

1. We shall have a wond'rous home in glo-ry,
2. All earth's sin and strife will then be end-ed, Some glad day,
3. Bless-ed tho't we'll sweet-ly rest for-ev-er,

Where we'll sing with saints the bless-ed sto-ry, Some glad
some glad day, When to heav-en's home we have as-cend-ed, Some glad
After we have crossed be-yond the riv-er, Some glad

Refrain

day when Je-sus comes. O............ how I long to meet Him!
When He comes, O how I long to meet Him!
O............ .... 'twill be joy to greet Him!
Glo-ry, glo-ry! 'twill be joy to greet Him!

Some glad day! some glad day! Some glad day when Je-sus comes.
(Omit............ ....)

No. 78. I Believe the Bible.

To Rev. G. W. Schurman, Pastor of Pentecostal Church, Lynn, Mass.

E. S. U. 3rd. verse by Rev. G. W. S.
Pastor E. S. UFFORD.

1. I be-lieve the Bi-ble, it taught me how to pray, Je-sus heard and answered,
2. I be-lieve the Bi-ble, it teach-es me to sing Mo-ses' song of vic-t'ry
3. I be-lieve the Bi-ble, of ho-li-ness it speaks, Gracious gift of Je-sus
4. I be-lieve the Bi-ble, it teach-es me to run In this roy-al high-way
5. Let us live the Bi-ble, and then the world will see We have been with Je-sus

took my sins a-way; Gave me peace and par-don, wrote my name a-bove,
o'er the ty-rant king; Or with Paul and Si-las, mid-night brings re-lease,
to the one who seeks; Tells of keep-ing pow-er 'neath the cleansing flood,
till the prize is won; Shows the crown a-wait-ing, if I win the race,
more like Him to be; With His word a-bid-ing in our hearts made new,

CHORUS.

Glo-ry hal-le-lu-jah! for His won-drous love.
Glo-ry hal-le-lu-jah! for His per-fect peace.
Glo-ry hal-le-lu-jah! for the pre-cious blood. I be-lieve the Bi-ble,
Glo-ry hal-le-lu-jah! for His sav-ing grace.
That will prove the blessed Book is al-ways true.

O it is di-vine! Heaven's golden sun-light in its pa-ges shine; Lights my way to glo-ry, and I'm sure-ly go-ing thro'; I be-lieve the Bi-ble, for 't is ev-er true.

Copyright, 1909, by E. S. Ufford, Rockland, Me. Used by permission.

No. 79 — **When We All Get to Heaven.**

E. E. Hewitt. Copyright, 1898, by Mrs. J. G. Wilson. Used by per. Mrs. J. G. Wilson.

1. Sing the won-drous love of Je-sus, Sing His mer-cy and His grace;
2. While we walk the pil-grim path-way, Clouds will o-ver-spread the sky;
3. Let us then be true and faith-ful, Trust-ing, serv-ing ev-'ry day;
4. On-ward to the prize be-fore us! Soon His beau-ty we'll be-hold;

In the man-sions, bright and blessed, He'll pre-pare for us a place.
But when trav-'ling days are o-ver, Not a shad-ow, not a sigh.
Just one glimpse of Him in glo-ry Will the toils of life re-pay.
Soon the pearl-y gates will o-pen, We shall tread the streets of gold.

CHORUS.

When we all get to heav-en, What a day of re-joic-ing that will be!
When we all   What a day of re-joic-ing that will be!

When we all see Je-sus, We'll sing and shout the vic-to-ry.
When we all   shout, and shout the vic-to-ry.

No. 80 The Sanctifying Power.

Rev. J. Oatman, Jr. Hamp Sewell.

1. When the sanc-ti-fy-ing pow-er of the Lord fell on my soul, I was filled, and I will praise Him all the day; What tho' dark a-bove my head storms of doubt and troub-le roll, I will rest and I will trust Him all the way.
2. When the sanc-ti-fy-ing pow-er of the Lord fell on my heart, I was cleans'd from all the weight of inbred sin; Then I felt the cleansing stream, felt the sense of guilt de-part, Felt that I was whol-ly sanc-ti-fied with-in.
3. When the sanc-ti-fy-ing pow-er of the Lord fell on my life, I was filled and thrilled with all the love of God; Now in-stead of in my life hav-ing ha-tred, en-vy, strife, In my soul the love of God is shed a-broad.
4. When the sanc-ti-fy-ing pow-er of the Lord fell on my soul, By the Ho-ly Ghost I was baptized with fire; Then my life was sealed for God, then my spir-it was made whole, Now I sing the songs they sing in heav-en's choir.

Chorus.

When the sanc-ti-fy-ing pow-er fell on me, when the power fell on me, When the sanc-ti-fy-ing pow-er fell on me; when the pow-er fell on me; O I love to tell the sto-ry, for He

Copyright Renewal, 1937. "Hymns of Glory," John T. Benson, Jr., Owner, Nashville, Tenn.

The Sanctifying Power. Concluded.

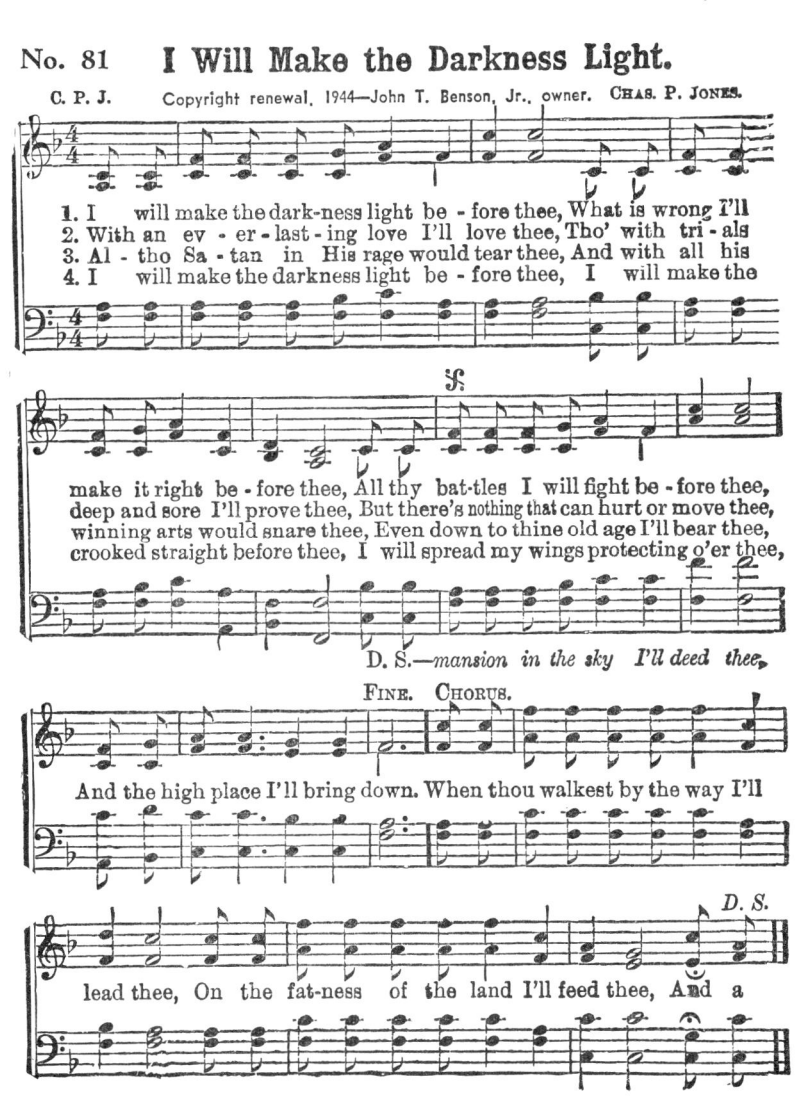

filled my soul with glo-ry, When the sanc-ti-fy-ing pow-er fell on me.

No. 81 I Will Make the Darkness Light.

C. P. J. Copyright renewal, 1944—John T. Benson, Jr., owner. CHAS. P. JONES.

1. I will make the dark-ness light be-fore thee, What is wrong I'll
2. With an ev-er-last-ing love I'll love thee, Tho' with tri-als
3. Al-tho Sa-tan in His rage would tear thee, And with all his
4. I will make the darkness light be-fore thee, I will make the

make it right be-fore thee, All thy bat-tles I will fight be-fore thee,
deep and sore I'll prove thee, But there's nothing that can hurt or move thee,
winning arts would snare thee, Even down to thine old age I'll bear thee,
crooked straight before thee, I will spread my wings protecting o'er thee,

D. S.—*mansion in the sky I'll deed thee.*

FINE. CHORUS.

And the high place I'll bring down. When thou walkest by the way I'll

lead thee, On the fat-ness of the land I'll feed thee, And a

No. 82. **The End Is Not Yet**

E. D. Elliott.
Wm. Edie Marks.

1. I have tried to count his bless-ings, and I fail to un-der-stand
2. Like an ar-my I be-hold them pass be-fore me in re-view,
3. Sure-ly good-ness, love and mer-cy have been mine a-long life's way,

Why the Lord should so rich-ly re-ward; Could I count the stars of heaven,
O what joy doth the sight now af-ford! Tho' they may be long in pass-ing,
And my weak heart to strength is restored; And my cup of joy and gladness

add to them earth's grains of sand, Still his blessings are more, praise the Lord!
still they come, battall-ions new, And the end is not yet, praise the Lord!
keeps o'er-flowing, day by day, And the end is not yet, praise the Lord!

CHORUS.

And the end is not yet, praise the Lord, And the end is not yet,
      praise the Lord,

praise the Lord; Blessings new he's still be-stow-ing. And my
O praise the Lord;

Copyright Renewal, 1934—John T. Benson, Jr., Owner

The End Is Not Yet—Concluded

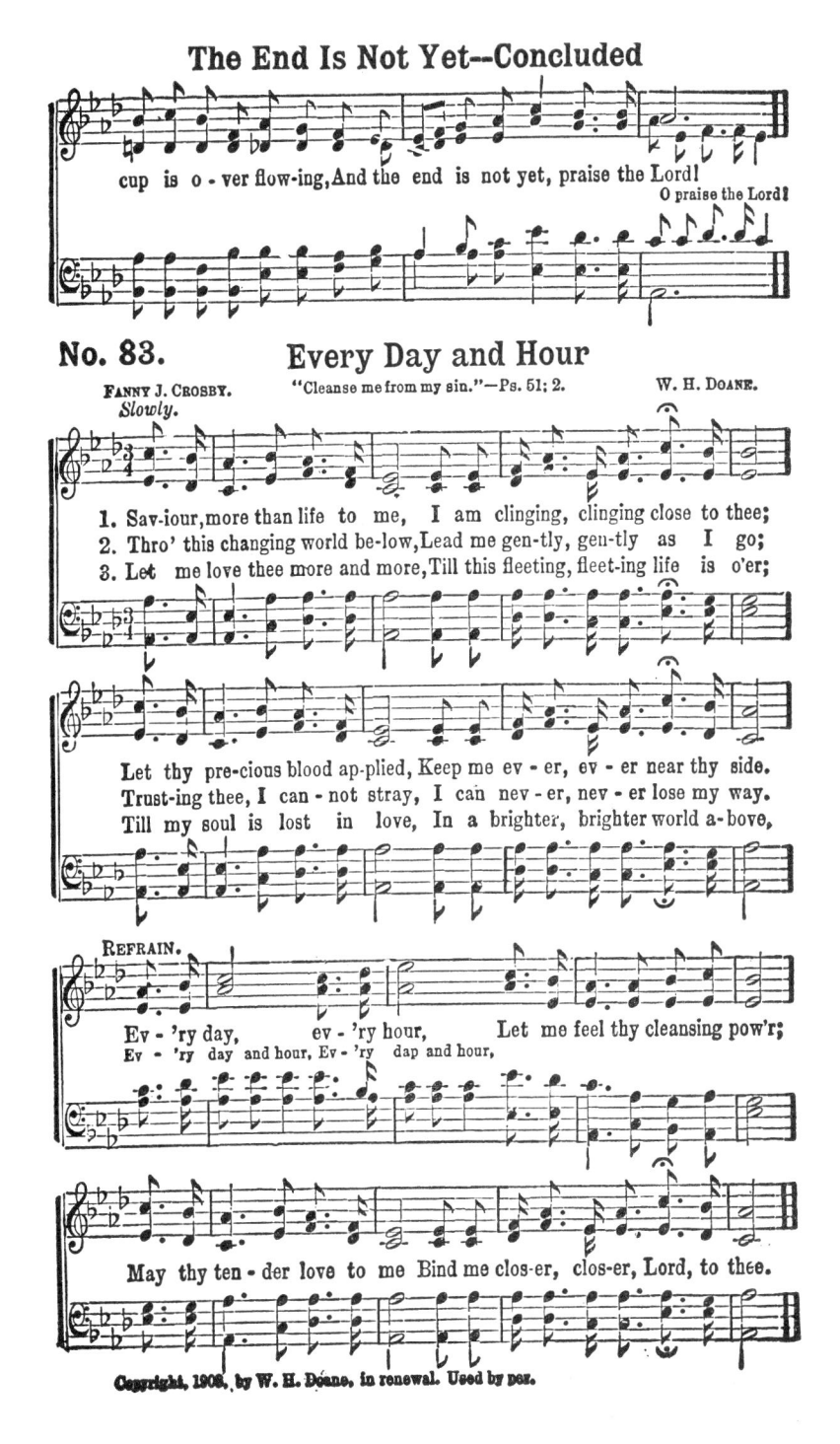

cup is o-ver flow-ing, And the end is not yet, praise the Lord!
O praise the Lord!

No. 83. Every Day and Hour

FANNY J. CROSBY. "Cleanse me from my sin."—Ps. 51; 2. W. H. DOANE.

Slowly.

1. Sav-iour, more than life to me, I am clinging, clinging close to thee;
2. Thro' this changing world be-low, Lead me gen-tly, gen-tly as I go;
3. Let me love thee more and more, Till this fleeting, fleet-ing life is o'er;

Let thy pre-cious blood ap-plied, Keep me ev - er, ev - er near thy side.
Trust-ing thee, I can - not stray, I can nev - er, nev - er lose my way.
Till my soul is lost in love, In a brighter, brighter world a-bove,

REFRAIN.

Ev - 'ry day, ev - 'ry hour, Let me feel thy cleansing pow'r;
Ev - 'ry day and hour, Ev - 'ry day and hour,

May thy ten - der love to me Bind me clos-er, clos-er, Lord, to thee.

Copyright, 1908, by W. H. Doane, in renewal. Used by per.

No. 84. The Hallelujah Side.

"Alleluia; salvation, and glory, and honor, and power, unto the Lord our God."—Rev. 19: 1.

REV. JOHNSON OATMAN, JR.   J. HOWARD ENTWISLE.

1. Once a sin-ner far from Je-sus, I was per-ish-ing with cold, But the
2. Tho' the world may sweep around me with her daz-zle and her dreams, Yet I
3. Not for all earth's golden millions would I leave this precious place, Tho' the
4. Here the sun is al-ways shining, here the sky is always bright; 'Tis no
5. And up-on the streets of glo-ry, when we reach the oth-er shore, And have

blessed Saviour heard me when I cried; Then He threw His robe around me, and He
en-vy not her van-i-ties and pride, For my soul looks up to heaven, where the
tempter to persuade me oft has tried, For I'm safe in God's pa-vil-ion, hap-py
place for gloomy Christians to a-bide, For my soul is filled with music and my
safely crossed the Jordan's rolling tide, You will find me shouting "Glory" just out-

Fine.

led me to His fold, And I'm liv-ing on the hal-le-lu-jah side.
gold-en sunlight gleams, And I'm liv-ing on the hal-le-lu-jah side.
in His love and grace, And I'm liv-ing on the hal-le-lu-jah side.
heart with great de-light, And I'm liv-ing on the hal-le-lu-jah side.
side my man-sion door, Where I'm liv-ing on the hal-le-lu-jah side.

D. S.—*win-dows of my soul, And I'm liv-ing on the hal-le-lu-jah side.*

CHORUS.

Oh, glo-ry be to Je-sus, let the hal-le-lu-jahs roll; Help me

D. S.

ring the Saviour's praises far and wide, For I've opened up tow'rd heaven all the

Copyright, 1898, by John J. Hood. By per.

No. 85 All Alone.

G. T. B. Copyright Owned by R. E. Winsett, G. T. BYRD.

1. On Mount Ol-ive's sa-cred brow Jesus spent the night in pray'r,
2. There are days I'd like to be With the sanc-ti-fied and blest,
3. There are days to fast and pray For the pil-grim in his way,
4. When a heart is brok-en up With the bit-ter, woe-ful cup,

He's the pat-tern for us all, all a-lone, If we'll on-ly steal a-way,
There are days I like to be all a-lone, These can nev-er grace impart,
There are days to be with Christ all a-lone, We can tell Him all our grief,
Then's the time to go to Christ all a-lone, In our bless-ed Lord di-vine,

In some por-tion of the day, We will find it al-ways pays to be a-lone.
To my weary, sin-toss'd heart, There are days I'd like to be just all a-lone.
He will give us quick re-lief, There are days I'd like to be just all a-lone.
There is peace and joy sublime, When we take our sorrows all to Him a-lone.

CHORUS.

There are days I'd like to be All a-lone with Christ my Lord,
I can tell Him of my troub-les all a-lone; all a-lone.

Copyright, 1904, by G. T. Byrd.

No. 86 **I Never Will Cease to Love Him.**

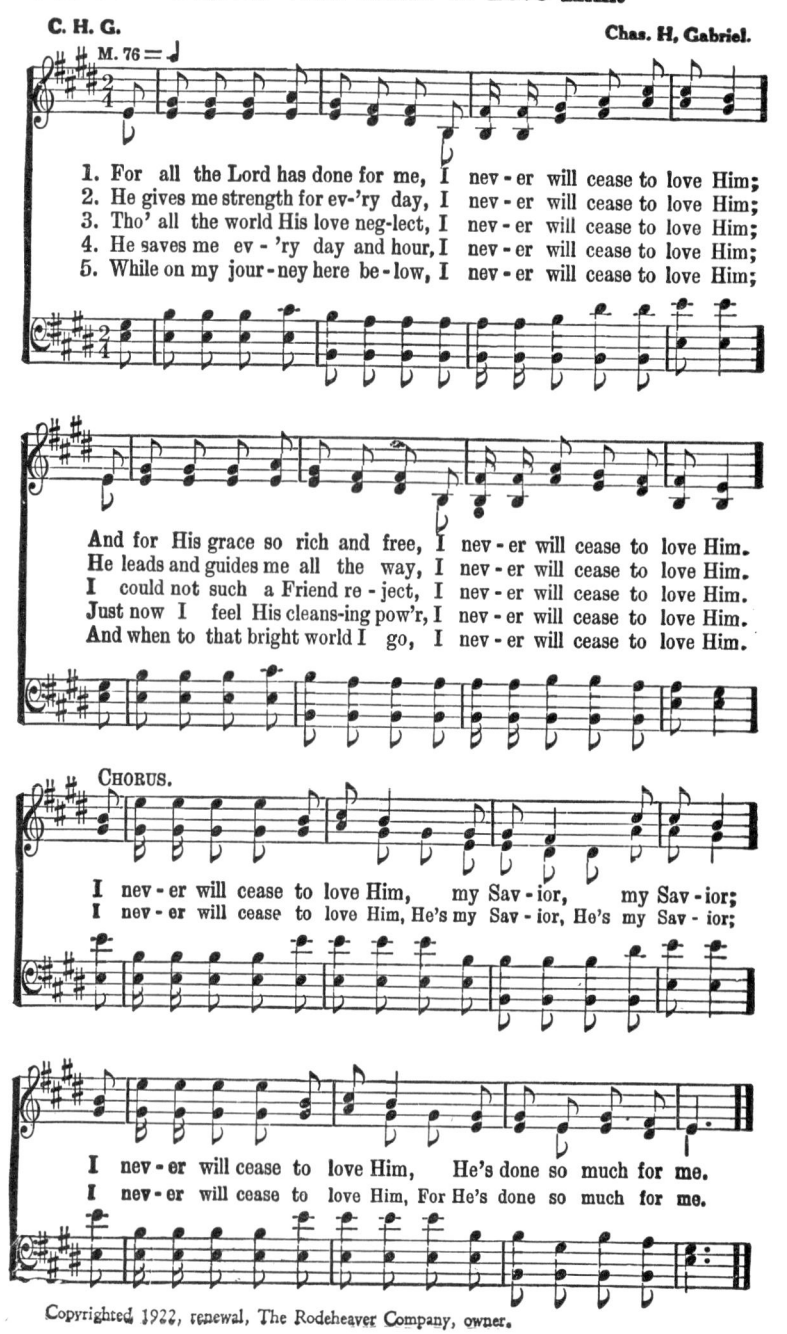

C. H. G.
Chas. H. Gabriel.

1. For all the Lord has done for me, I nev-er will cease to love Him;
2. He gives me strength for ev-'ry day, I nev-er will cease to love Him;
3. Tho' all the world His love neg-lect, I nev-er will cease to love Him;
4. He saves me ev-'ry day and hour, I nev-er will cease to love Him;
5. While on my jour-ney here be-low, I nev-er will cease to love Him;

And for His grace so rich and free, I nev-er will cease to love Him.
He leads and guides me all the way, I nev-er will cease to love Him.
I could not such a Friend re-ject, I nev-er will cease to love Him.
Just now I feel His cleans-ing pow'r, I nev-er will cease to love Him.
And when to that bright world I go, I nev-er will cease to love Him.

CHORUS.

I nev-er will cease to love Him, my Sav-ior, my Sav-ior;
I nev-er will cease to love Him, He's my Sav-ior, He's my Sav-ior;

I nev-er will cease to love Him, He's done so much for me.
I nev-er will cease to love Him, For He's done so much for me.

Copyrighted 1922, renewal, The Rodeheaver Company, owner.

No. 87 **The Old Rugged Cross**

G. B.
SOLO AND CHORUS.
Copyrighted 1941, renewal,
The Rodeheaver Company, owner.
Rev. Geo. Bennard.

1. On a hill far a-way stood an old rug-ged cross, The em-blem of suf-f'ring and shame, And I love that old cross where the dear-est and best For a world of lost sin-ners was slain.
2. Oh, that old rug-ged cross, so de-spised by the world, Has a wondrous at-trac-tion for me, For the dear Lamb of God left His glo-ry a-bove, To bear it to dark Cal-va-ry.
3. In the old rug-ged cross, stained with blood so di-vine, A won-drous beau-ty I see; For 'twas on that old cross Je-sus suf-fered and died, To par-don and sanc-ti-fy me.
4. To the old rug-ged cross I will ev-er be true, Its shame and re-proach glad-ly bear; Then He'll call me some day to my home far a-way, Where His glo-ry for-ev-er I'll share.

CHORUS.

So I'll cher-ish the old rug-ged cross, the old rug-ged cross, Till my tro-phies at last I lay down; I will cling to the old rug-ged cross, the old rug-ged cross, And ex-change it some day for a crown.

No. 88   Nothing Like Jesus.

"Whom have I in heaven but thee, and there is none I desire on earth beside thee."—Ps. 73.

C. P. J.   Chas. P. Jones.

1. There is noth-ing in the world like Je-sus, He's the treas-ure of my soul;
2. There is noth-ing in the world like Je-sus, He sup-plies my ev-'ry need;
3. Ev-'ry tri-al of my life I tell Him, And He un-der-stands it well;
4. O there's no one in the world like Je-sus, Sym-pa-thet-ic, kind and true;
5. Have you troubles in your life, my broth-er? Does your heart ache day by day?

When I'm troubled He dis-pels my sor-rows, When I'm sick He makes me whole.
And when oth-ers, whom I trust, be-tray me, He re-mains a friend in-deed.
He sus-tains me with His con-so-la-tion, Ev-'ry fear His words dis-pel.
If it was not that I know and trust Him, I know not what I should do.
If you'll bring your burdens all to Je-sus, He will bear them all a-way.

Chorus.

O I love to tell the mer-its of my Sav-iour, Ev-'ry soul I can to win; O I love to tell the sto-ry of His pow-er, How He saves and keeps from sin.

Copyright Renewal, 1941, John T. Benson, Jr., Owner

Wonderful Peace.

No. 89

Copyright, 1914, by Charles Reign Scoville.
International copyright secured.

H. L.
Haldor Lillenas.

1. Com-ing to Je-sus, my Sav-iour, I found Won-der-ful peace,
2. Peace like a riv-er, so deep and so broad, Won-der-ful peace,
3. Peace like a ho-ly and in-fi-nite calm, Won-der-ful peace,
4. Gone is the bat-tle that once raged with-in, Won-der-ful peace,

won-der-ful peace; Storms in their fu-ry may rage all a-
won-der-ful peace; Rest-ing my soul on the bos-om of
won-der-ful peace; Like to the strain of an e-ven-ing
won-der-ful peace; Je-sus has saved me and cleansed me from

REFRAIN.

round, I have peace, sweet peace.
God, I have peace, sweet peace. Peace, peace, won-der-ful peace,
psalm, I have peace, sweet peace.
sin, I have peace, sweet peace.

Peace, peace, glo-ri-ous peace, Since my Re-deem-er has

ran-somed my soul I have peace, sweet peace............
won-der-ful peace.

No. 90. Press Along to Glory-Land.

JAMES ROWE.
EMMETT S. DEAN.

1. O ransomed souls, with joyous song Press a-long to Glo-ry-land;
   Ex-tolling grace that saves the race, Press a-long to Glo-ry-land.
2. The foe may rave, but Christ will save,
   The storm may sweep, but He will keep,
3. To join once more those gone be-fore,
   With saints to sing be-fore the King,
4. The crown to wear for-ev-er there, Press a-long
   To sing His praise thro' countless days, Press a-long

CHORUS.

Press a-long, (Press a-long,) glad soul, press a-long, Giv-ing out (Giv-ing out) the mes-sage grand; Let-ting love, (Let-ting love,) God's love, be your song, Press a-long (Press a-long) to Glo-ry-land.

Copyright 1939, Renewal, John T. Benson, Jr., owner.

COVERED BY THE BLOOD

"Blessed is he whose iniquities are forgiven and whose sins are under the blood."

NELLIE EDWARDS.   RAN. C. STOREY.

Not too fast.

1. Once in sin's darkest night, I was wand'ring alone, A stranger to mercy I stood; But the Saviour came nigh, When He heard my faint cry, And He put my sins un-der the blood.
2. From my errors and faults, Jesus saves me so free, Amazed that He lifted my load; O the love and the grace I received in its place, When He put my sins un-der the blood.
3. I can ne'er understand Why He sought even me, Why His life-blood on Calv'ry flowed; But sufficient for me, Since He died on the tree, He hath put my sins un-der the blood.
4. Now He comes to my heart And removes ev'ry care, For He bears all my cumb'ring load; In a pathway replete With His love are my feet, Since He put my sins un-der the blood.

REFRAIN.

They are covered by the blood, They are cov-ered by the blood, My sins are all cov-ered by the blood, Mine in-iq-ui-ties so vast, (precious blood,) Have been blotted out at last, My sins are all cov-ered by the blood. (precious blood.)

Copyright, 1932, by Jos. M. Black—Nazarene Pub. House, Owner.

No. 92. Send the Light.

C. H. G.
COPYRIGHT, 1890, BY CHAS. H. GABRIEL
Chas. H. Gabriel.

1. There's a call comes ring-ing o'er the rest-less wave, "Send the light!
2. We have heard the Mac-e-do-nian call to-day, "Send the light!
3. Let us pray that grace may ev-'ry-where a-bound; Send the light!
4. Let us not grow wear-y in the work of love; Send the light!

Send the light!" There are souls to res-cue, there are souls to save,
Send the light!" And a gold-en of-f'ring at the cross we lay,
Send the light! And a Christ-like spir-it ev-'ry-where be found,
Send the light! Let us gath-er jew-els for a crown a-bove,

Refrain.

Send the light!...... Send the light!...... Send the light!...... the
blessed gos-pel light; Let it shine...... from shore to shore!...... shine...... for-ev-er-more......

No. 93 STANDING ON THE PROMISES

R. K. C.   R. Kelso Carter.

1. Standing on the prom-is-es of Christ my King, Thro' e-ter-nal a-ges let His prais-es ring; Glo-ry in the high-est, I will shout and sing,
2. Standing on the prom-is-es that can-not fail, When the howl-ing storms of doubt and fear as-sail; By the liv-ing Word of God, I shall pre-vail,
3. Standing on the prom-is-es, I now can see Per-fect, pres-ent cleansing in the blood for me; Standing in the lib-er-ty where Christ makes free,
4. Standing on the prom-is-es of Christ the Lord, Bound to Him e-ter-nal-ly by love's strong cord; O-ver-com-ing dai-ly with the Spir-it's sword,
5. Standing on the prom-is-es I can-not fall, Lis-t'ning ev-'ry mo-ment to the Spir-it's call; Rest-ing in my Sav-ior, as my all in all,

CHORUS.

Standing on the prom-is-es of God. Stand - ing, stand - ing,
Standing on the promise, standing on the promise,
Standing on the prom-is-es of God, my Sav-ior; Stand - ing,
Standing on the promise,
stand - ing, I'm stand-ing on the prom-is-es of God.
standing on the promise,

COPYRIGHT, 1886, BY JOHN J. HOOD. USED BY PER.

No. 94 My Redeemer

COPYRIGHT, 1908, BY JAMES MCGRANAHAN. RENEWAL.
CHARLES M. ALEXANDER, OWNER.

P. P. Bliss. James McGranahan.

1. I will sing of my Re-deem-er, And His won-drous love to me;
2. I will tell the won-drous sto-ry, How my lost es-tate to save,
3. I will praise my dear Re-deem-er, His tri-um-phant pow'r I'll tell,
4. I will sing of my Re-deem-er, And His heav'n-ly love to me;

On the cru-el cross He suf-fered, From the curse to set me free.
In His boundless love and mer-cy, He the ran-som free-ly gave.
How the vic-to-ry He giv-eth O-ver sin, and death, and hell.
He from death to life hath brought me, Son of God with Him to be.

CHORUS.

Sing, oh, sing.......... of my Re-deem-er, With His
Sing, oh, sing of my Re-deem er, Sing, oh, sing of my Re-deem-er,

blood....... He purchased me,....... On the cross..... He sealed my
He purchased me, With His blood He purchased me, He sealed my pardon, On the

Repeat pp after last verse.

par-don, Paid the debt........ and made me free.........
cross He sealed my pardon, Paid the debt and made me free, and made me free.

No. 95 WE'RE MARCHING TO ZION

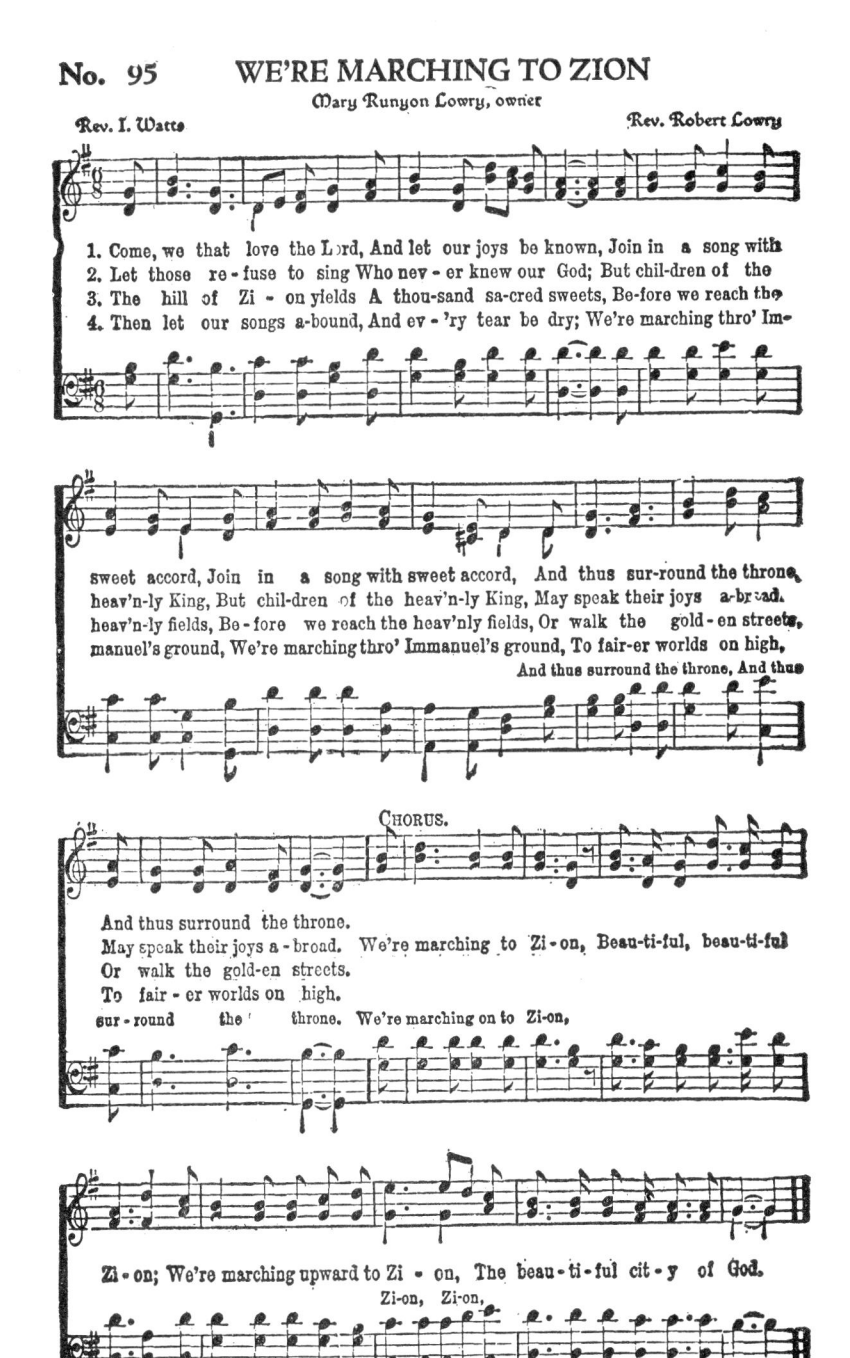

Mary Runyon Lowry, owner

Rev. I. Watts
Rev. Robert Lowry

1. Come, we that love the Lord, And let our joys be known, Join in a song with sweet accord, Join in a song with sweet accord, And thus sur-round the throne.
2. Let those re-fuse to sing Who nev-er knew our God; But chil-dren of the heav'n-ly King, But chil-dren of the heav'n-ly King, May speak their joys a-broad.
3. The hill of Zi-on yields A thou-sand sa-cred sweets, Be-fore we reach the heav'n-ly fields, Be-fore we reach the heav'nly fields, Or walk the gold-en streets.
4. Then let our songs a-bound, And ev-'ry tear be dry; We're marching thro' Im-manuel's ground, We're marching thro' Immanuel's ground, To fair-er worlds on high,

And thus surround the throne, And thus

And thus surround the throne.
May speak their joys a-broad.
Or walk the gold-en streets.
To fair-er worlds on high.
sur-round the throne.

CHORUS.

We're marching to Zi-on, Beau-ti-ful, beau-ti-ful Zi-on; We're marching upward to Zi-on, The beau-ti-ful cit-y of God.

We're marching on to Zi-on, Zi-on, Zi-on,

No. 96   TELL IT TO JESUS ALONE

J. E. Rankin, D.D.   Rev. E. S. Lorenz, by per.

1. Are you wea-ry, are you heav-y-heart-ed? Tell it to Je-sus,
2. Do the tears flow down your cheeks un-bid-den? Tell it to Je-sus,
3. Do you fear the gath'ring clouds of sor-row? Tell it to Je-sus,
4. Are you troub-led at the tho't of dy-ing? Tell it to Je-sus,

Tell it to Je-sus; Are you griev-ing o-ver joys de-part-ed?
Tell it to Je-sus; Have you sins that to man's eyes are hid-den?
Tell it to Je-sus; Are you anx-ious what shall be to-mor-row?
Tell it to Je-sus; For Christ's com-ing King-dom are you sigh-ing?

CHORUS.

Tell it to Je-sus a-lone. Tell it to Je-sus, Tell it to Je-sus, He is a friend that's well known; You have no oth-er such a friend or broth-er; Tell it to Je-sus a-lone.

No. 97. The "Haven of Rest."

"For we which have believed do enter into rest."—Hebrews 4: 3.

H. L. GILMOUR. GEO. D. MOORE.

1. My soul in sad ex-ile was out on life's sea, So burdened with sin, and dis-trest, Till I heard a sweet voice say-ing, "Make me your choice;" And I en-tered the "Ha-ven of Rest."
2. I yield-ed my-self to His ten-der em-brace, And, faith tak-ing hold of the word, My fet-ters fell off, and I an-chored my soul; The "Ha-ven of Rest" is my Lord.
3. The song of my soul, since the Lord made me whole, Has been the old sto-ry so blest, Of Je-sus, who'll save who-so-ev-er will have A home in the "Ha-ven of Rest."
4. How pre-cious the tho't that we all may re-cline, Like John, the be-lov-ed and blest, On Je-sus' strong arm, where no tem-pest can harm, Se-cure in the "Ha-ven of Rest!"
5. Oh, come to the Sav-iour, He pa-tient-ly waits To save by His pow-er di-vine; Come, an-chor your soul in the "Ha-ven of Rest," And say, "My Be-lov-ed is mine."

D. S.—The tem-pest may sweep o'er the wild, storm-y deep, In Je-sus I'm safe ev-er-more.

CHORUS.

I've anchored my soul in the "Haven of Rest," I'll sail the wide seas no more;

Copyright, by John J. Hood. By per.

No. 98   I Am So Glad.

JAMES ROWE.   J. E. THOMAS.

1. I am so glad salvation's free to all who will receive it,
Glad that the news was bro't to me when I was lost and sad;
Praise His dear name, I can proclaim that truly I believe it,
For I am now His child, I know, and I'm so glad.

2. I am so glad that I can tell to wayward souls the story,
Glad that by grace from day to day a helper I may be;
Finding delight in service true, my soul is winning glory,
Glory for Him who gave His life to rescue me.

3. I am so glad that all my heart to Jesus I have given,
Glad that at eventide my soul true sheaves to Him may bring;
I will be true until with all the happy throng in heaven,
Sweeter and nobler praise I give to Christ, my King.

REFRAIN.

Glory, glory and honor, be to His name forever, Never a greater honor,

Copyright, 1913, words and music by J. E. Thomas.

I Am So Glad. Concluded.

Friend the sinful race has had.... Love Him, Praise Him,
Love Him and serve Him, Love Him and Praise Him,
Jesus, the matchless Saviour, He has redeemed this soul of mine, And I'm so glad.

No. 99 Unsearchable Riches.

F. J. C. J. R. Sweney.

1. O the un-search-a-ble rich-es of Christ! Wealth that can never be told;
2. O the un-search-a-ble rich-es of Christ, Who shall their greatness de-clare;
3. O the un-search-a-ble rich-es of Christ, Free-ly, how free-ly they flow;
4. O the un-search-a-ble rich-es of Christ, Who would not glad-ly en-dure

Rich-es ex-haustless of mer-cy and grace, Precious, more precious than gold.
Jew-els whose lus-ter our lives may a-dorn, Pearls that the poorest may wear.
Mak-ing the souls of the faith-ful and true, Hap-py wher-ev-er they go.
Tri-als, af-flic-tions and cross-es on earth, Rich-es like these to se-cure?

D. S.—O the un-search-a-ble rich-es of Christ! Precious, more precious than gold!

CHORUS.

Pre-cious, more pre-cious, Wealth that can nev-er be told;

No. 100

The Lord Is My Shepherd

T. KOSCHAT.

Lento.

1. The Lord is my Shep-herd, no want shall I know; I feed in green pas-tures, safe-fold-ed I rest; He lead-eth my soul where the still wa-ters flow, Re - stores me when wand'ring, re - deems when oppressed; Re - stores me when wand'ring, redeems when oppressed.

2. Thro' the val - ley and shad - ow of death tho' I stray, Since Thou art my Guar-dian, no e - vil I fear; Thy rod shall de - fend me, Thy staff be my stay; No harm can be - fall, with my Com - fort er near; No harm can be - fall, with my Com-fort - er near.

3. In the midst of af - flic - tion my ta - ble is spread; With bless-ings un - meas-ured my cup run - neth o'er; With per - fume and oil Thou a - noint-est my head; Oh, what shall I ask of Thy prov - i-dence more? Oh, what shall I ask of Thy prov-i-dence more.

4. Let good - ness and mer - cy, my boun - ti - ful God, Still fol - low my steps till I meet Thee a - bove. I seek by the path which my fore - fa - thers trod, Thro' the land of their so-journ, Thy king - dom of love; Thro' the land of their so-journ, Thy kingdom of love.

No. 101 **The Half has Never been Told.**

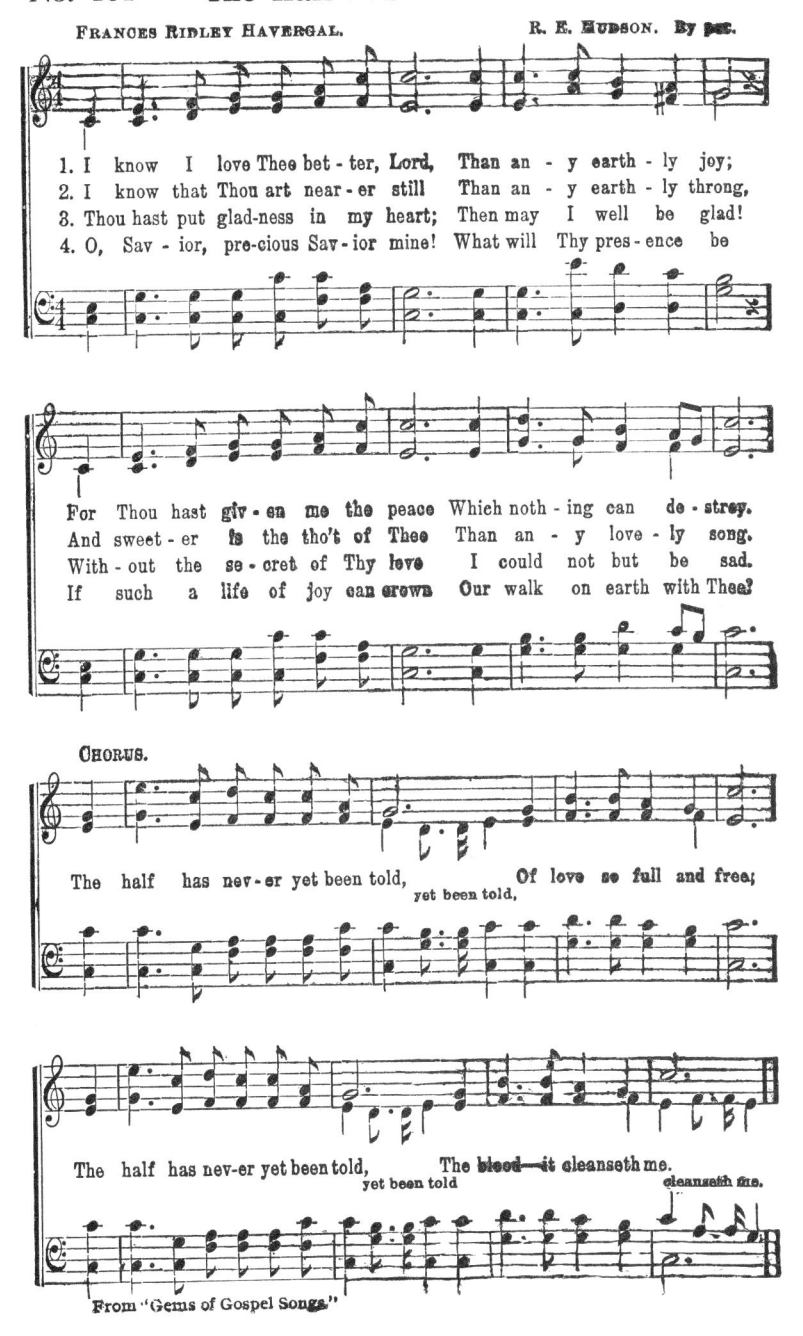

FRANCES RIDLEY HAVERGAL. R. E. HUDSON. By per.

1. I know I love Thee bet-ter, Lord, Than an-y earth-ly joy;
2. I know that Thou art near-er still Than an-y earth-ly throng,
3. Thou hast put glad-ness in my heart; Then may I well be glad!
4. O, Sav-ior, pre-cious Sav-ior mine! What will Thy pres-ence be

For Thou hast giv-en me the peace Which noth-ing can de-stroy.
And sweet-er is the tho't of Thee Than an-y love-ly song.
With-out the se-cret of Thy love I could not but be sad.
If such a life of joy can crown Our walk on earth with Thee?

CHORUS.

The half has nev-er yet been told, *yet been told,* Of love so full and free;

The half has nev-er yet been told, *yet been told* The blood—it cleanseth me. *cleanseth me.*

From "Gems of Gospel Songs."

No. 102 CONSECRATED TALENTS.

Mrs. M. A. S.
Mrs. Minnie A. Steele.

1. Do you love the Sav-ior who's done so much for you? Con-se-crate your tal-ents to Him; Bring them to the Mas-ter and see what He will do, Con-se-crate your tal-ents to Him.
2. Are your tal-ents hid-den? O bring them to the light, Con-se-crate your tal-ents to Him; He will give the se-cret of mak-ing tal-ents bright, Con-se-crate your tal-ents to Him.
3. Would you ne'er be i-dle? this ver-y day be-gin, Con-se-crate your tal-ents to Him; Would you seek the stray-ing, some pre-cious souls to win? Con-se-crate your tal-ents to Him.

Chorus.

Con-se-crat-ed tal-ents, how they shine, Touched by the glory of the love di-vine; Con-se-crat-ed tal-ents, do you know, Help in mak-ing heav-en on earth be-low?

Copyright, 1909, by I. G. Martin. Used by permission.

No. 103   Come to the Feast.

Copyright, 1895, by Chas. H. Gabriel.

CHARLOTTE G. HOMER.   W. E. M. Hackleman, owner.   W. A. OGDEN.

1. "All things are ready," come to the feast! Come, for the ta-ble now is spread; Ye famishing, ye wea-ry, come, And thou shalt be richly fed.
2. "All things are ready," come to the feast! Come, for the door is o-pen wide; A place of hon-or is re-serv'd For you at the Master's side.
3. "All things are ready," come to the feast! Come, while He waits to welcome thee; De-lay not while this day is thine, To-mor-row may nev-er be.
4. "All things are ready," come to the feast! Leave ev-'ry care and worldly strife; Come, feast upon the love of God, And drink ev-er-last-ing life.

CHORUS.

Hear......... the in-vi-ta-tion, Come, "who--so--ev-er will;"............ Praise God.......... for full sal-va--tion For "who-so-ev-er will."
Hear the in-vi-ta-tion, "Who-so-ev-er will," Hear the in-vi-ta-tion, "Who-so-ev-er will;" Praise God for full sal-va-tion For "who-so-ev-er will,"

No. 104 My Sheep Know My Voice

First stanza, chorus and melody by H. BUFFUM. *Arr. by I. G. MARTIN.*

1. My sheep know my voice, And the path that I take, They fol-low where-ev-er I go; My sheep know my voice And come at my call, But a stranger's voice do they not know.

2. My sheep know my voice, And the pas-tures of green, Where I lead them so oft-en to feed; My sheep know my voice And the cool sparkling stream Where be-side its still wa-ters I lead.

3. My sheep know my voice, And the val-ley of death Thro' which I shall lead them some day; But no dan-ger nor harm Can touch one of them, For I will be with them al-way.

Chorus.

My sheep .... know my voice, ... And day .... by day, ... They a-bide ...... in the fold .... And go .... not a-stray, ... They love .... me be-

My sheep know my voice, day by day, My sheep know my voice day by day, They a-bide in the fold, They go not a-stray, A-bide in the fold, They go not a-stray, They love me be-cause I

Copyright, 1906, by I. G. Martin.

My Sheep Know My Voice. Concluded.

cause......... I have made....... them my choice,....... And they
made them my choice, They love me be-cause I made them my choice, They

fol - low my call,......... For my sheep know my voice.
fol-low my call, They fol-low my call, my sheep know my voice.

No. 105 All for Jesus.

MARY D. JAMES. ARRANGED.

1. { All for Je-sus, all for Je - sus! All my being's ransomed pow'rs;
   { All my thot's, and words, and doings, All my days, and all my hours.
2. { Let my hands perform His bid-ding, Let my feet run in His ways—
   { Let my eyes see Je-sus on - ly, Let my lips speak forth His praise.

All for Je-sus! all for Je - sus! All my days and all my hours; hours.
All for Je-sus! all for Je - sus! Let my lips speak forth His praise; praise.

3 Since my eyes were fixed on Jesus,
   I've lost sight of all beside;
So enchained my spirit's vision,
   Looking at the Crucified.
All for Jesus! all for Jesus!
   Looking at the Crucified;

4 Oh, what wonder! how amazing!
   Jesus, glorious King of kings—
Deigns to call me His beloved,
   Lets me rest beneath His wings.
All for Jesus! all for Jesus!
   Resting now beneath His wings;

No. 106 **Living by Faith.**

Owned by R. E. Winsett, East Chattanooga, Tenn.

JAMES WELLS. 4 v. R. E. W. J. L. HEATH.

1. I care not to-day what the morrow may bring, If shadow or sunshine or rain,
2. Tho' tempests may blow and the storm-clouds arise, Obscuring the brightness of life,
3. I know that He safely will carry me thro', No matter what e-vils be-tide,
4. Our Lord will return to this earth some sweet day, Our troubles will then all be o'er,

The Lord I know rul-eth o'er ev-er-y-thing, And all of my wor-ry is vain.
I'm nev-er a-larmed at the overcast skies, The Master looks on at the strife.
Why should I then care, tho' the tempest may blow, If Je-sus walks close to my side.
The Mas-ter so gent-ly will lead us a-way, Beyond that blest heav'nly shore.

REFRAIN.

Liv-ing by faith,............ in Je-sus a-bove,............
Yes, liv-ing by faith, in Je-sus a-bove,

Trusting, con-fid - - - ing in His great love;............
Trusting, con-fid-ing yes, in His great love;

From all harm safe............ in His shel-ter-ing arm,............
Safe from all harm, safe His shel-ter-ing arm,

Living by Faith. Concluded.

I'm liv-ing by faith............ and feel no a-larm......
I'm liv-ing by faith   feel no a-larm.

No. 107 **I WOULD NOT BE DENIED.**

C. P. JONES.

1. When pangs of death seized on my soul, Un-to the Lord I cried,
2. As Ja-cob in the days of old, I wres-tled with the Lord;
3. Old Sa-tan said my Lord was gone, And would not hear my prayer;

Till Je-sus came and made me whole; I would not be de-nied.
And in-stant, with a cour-age bold, I stood up-on His word.
But, praise the Lord! the work is done, And Christ the Lord is here.

CHORUS.

I would not be de-nied (de-nied), I would not be de-nied (de-nied),

Till Je-sus came and made me whole; I would not be de-nied.
de-nied.

Copyright, 1900, by C. P. Jones. Used by per.

No. 108 **Jesus Saves.**

PRISCILLA J. OWENS. WM. J. KIRKPATRICK.

1. We have heard the joy-ful sound, Je-sus saves, Je-sus saves;
2. Waft it on the roll-ing tide, Je-sus saves, Je-sus saves;
3. Sing a-bove the bat-tle's strife, Je-sus saves, Je-sus saves;
4. Give the winds a might-y voice, Je-sus saves, Je-sus saves;

Spread the glad-ness all a-round, Je-sus saves, Je-sus saves;
Tell to sin-ners far and wide, Je-sus saves, Je-sus saves;
By his death and end-less life, Je-sus saves, Je-sus saves;
Let the na-tions now re-joice, Je-sus saves, Je-sus saves;

Bear the news to ev-'ry land, Climb the steeps and cross the waves,
Sing, ye is-lands of the sea, Ech-o back, ye o-cean caves,
Sing it soft-ly thro' the gloom, When the heart for mer-cy craves,
Shout sal-va-tion full and free, High-est hills and deep-est caves,

On-ward, 'tis our Lord's command, Je-sus saves, Je-sus saves.
Earth shall keep her ju-bi-lee, Je-sus saves, Je-sus saves.
Sing in tri-umph o'er the tomb, Je-sus saves, Je-sus saves.
This our song of vic-to-ry, Je-sus saves, Je-sus saves.

No. 109 Holding On!

W. E. M.   Wm. Edie Marks.

1. Ev - er since my Saviour washed my sins a - way, I have close-ly fol-lowed Him from day to day; I'm de - ter-mined with Him I will ev - er stay.
2. Holding on to Je - sus with a faith su - preme, And the sunbeams of His love a - round me gleam, Gain-ing blessings far be-yond my fond - est dream.
3. Storms may come and storms may go, He holds me fast, Safe - ly sheltered from the cold and storm - y blast; I will fol - low where He leads me to the last.

CHORUS.

Hal - le - lu - jah, I am hold - ing on! Hold - ing on, my heart's se-cure, Love will o-ver-come, endure, Hold - ing on, re-ward is sure. Hal - le - lu - jah, I am hold-ing on!

Hold-ing on to Je - sus, now my heart's se-cure, Love and faith will ev - er o-ver-come, endure, Hold-ing on to Je - sus, my re - ward is sure!

Copyright Renewal, 1935, in "Full of Blessing No. 3"—John T. Benson, Jr., Owner

No. 110 I Hold Fast to Jesus.

Copyright Renewal 1944 in "Full of Blessing No. 3"
John T. Benson, Jr., Owner

James Rowe.   Wm. Edie Marks.

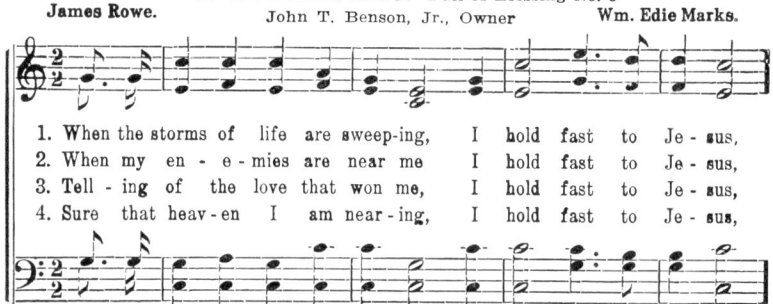

1. When the storms of life are sweep-ing, I hold fast to Je-sus,
2. When my en-e-mies are near me I hold fast to Je-sus,
3. Tell-ing of the love that won me, I hold fast to Je-sus,
4. Sure that heav-en I am near-ing, I hold fast to Je-sus,

Al-ways safe in His dear keep-ing, I hold fast to Je-sus.
Sure that He will shield and cheer me, I hold fast to Je-sus.
With His lov-ing smile up-on me, I hold fast to Je-sus.
An-gel voi-ces ev-er hear-ing, I hold fast to Je-sus.

CHORUS.

I hold fast, I hold fast, Though the
I hold fast, hold fast, hold fast, I hold fast, hold fast,

waves may roll, He will keep my soul, I hold fast to Je-sus!

No. 111 MY SOUL IS FILLED WITH GLORY.

J. M. H.   J. M. Harris.

1. Je-sus found me when a-far I wandered, Bro't me pardon from the throne a-bove; Gave me peace that passeth un-der-stand-ing, Joy unspeak-a-ble and full of love.
2. Thro' His word He taught me full sal-va-tion, How His blood could cleanse and sanc-ti-fy; Then by faith I plunged in-to the foun-tain; Now I'm look-ing for that home on high.
3. Tri-als man-y will be-set my path-way, And tempta-tions I shall sure-ly meet; But my Saviour promised grace to help me, Till I lay my trophies at His feet.

Chorus.

Praise the Lord! my soul is filled with glo-ry! Praise the Lord! I love to tell the sto-ry, Of His grace that jus-ti-fies me free-ly, And I'm shouting glo-ry! till I get home.

Praise the Lord! my soul is filled with glo-ry! Praise the Lord! I love to tell the sto-ry, Of His grace that sanc-ti-fies me whol-ly, And I'm shouting glo-ry! till I get home.

Praise the Lord! my soul is filled with glo-ry! Praise the Lord! I love to tell the sto-ry, Of His grace that keeps, and gives me vict'ry, And I'm shouting glo-ry! till I get home.

Copyright, 1905, by J. M. Harris, Evanston, Ill. Used by per.

No. 112   What a Wonderful Day

H. L.   Haldor Lillenas

1. What a won-der-ful day when I lost the load I had car-ried so long on life's wear-y road; All my sins blot-ted out, gone my fear and doubt, won-der-ful, won-der-ful day!
2. What a won-der-ful day with a heart made new I be-gan a new life with the cross in view; My am-bi-tions were changed, from the world es-tranged, What a won-der-ful, won-der-ful day!
3. What a won-der-ful day when the Lord shall come with the sound of the trum-pet to take us home; When with Him we shall dwell, our Im-man-u-el,

CHORUS.

What a won-der-ful day, when my bur-dens rolled a-way, And the Saviour came in to dwell; He's my Comforter and Guide, Dai-ly walk-ing by my side, Hal-le-lu-jah, hal-le-lu-jah all is well

Copyright 1946, in "Church and Radio Songs." John T. Benson. Jr., owner.

No. 113 NEVER ALONE

1. I've seen the lightning flashing, And heard the thunder roll—
   I've heard the voice of Jesus, Telling me still to fight on,
2. The world's fierce winds are blowing Temptations sharp and keen—
   He stands to shield me from danger, When earthly friends are gone,
3. When in affliction's valley I'm treading the road of care,
   My feet entangled with briars Ready to cast me down,
4. He died for me on the mountain—For me they pierced His side—
   For me He's waiting in glory, Seated upon His throne,

I've felt sin's breakers dashing— Trying to conquer my soul—
He promised never to leave me,— [Omit.
I feel a peace in knowing—My Saviour stands between,
He promised never to leave me, [Omit.
My Saviour helps me to carry My cross when heavy to bear,
My Saviour whispers His promise: "I [Omit.
For me He opened that fountain, The crimson, cleansing tide,
He promised never to leave me, [Omit.

CHORUS

Never to leave me alone.
Never to leave me alone. No, never alone,— No never a-
"Never will leave thee alone."
Never to leave me alone.

lone, He promised never to leave me— Never to leave me alone.

114. Victory In Jesus

Copyright, 1939, E. M. Bartlett
Stamps-Baxter Music & Ptg. Co., owners

E. M. B.
E. M. BARTLETT

1. I heard an old, old sto-ry, how a Sav-ior came from glo-ry,
How He gave His life on Cal-va-ry to save a wretch like me;
I heard a-bout His groan-ing, of His pre-cious blood's a-ton-ing,
Then I re-pent-ed of my sins and won the vic-to-ry.

2. I heard a-bout His heal-ing, of His cleansing pow'r re-veal-ing,
How He made the lame to walk a-gain and caused the blind to see;
And then I cried "dear Je-sus, come and heal my bro-ken spir-it,"
And some-how Je-sus came and bro't to me the vic-to-ry.

3. I heard a-bout a man-sion He has built for me in glo-ry,
And I heard a-bout the streets of gold be-yond the crys-tal sea;
A-bout the an-gels sing-ing, and the old re-demp-tion sto-ry,
And some sweet day I'll sing up there the song of vic-to-ry.

Chorus

O vic-to-ry in Je-sus, my Sav-ior, for-ev-er, He sought me and

Victory In Jesus Concluded

bo't me with His re-deem-ing blood; He loved me ere I knew Him, and all my love is due Him, He plunged me to vic-to-ry, be-neath the cleansing flood.

115 Precious Memories

J.B. F. W. Stamps-Baxter Music Co., owners. J. B. F. WRIGHT

1. Pre-cious mem'ries, un-seen an-gels, Sent from somewhere to my soul;
2. Pre-cious fa-ther, lov-ing moth-er, Fly a-cross the lone-ly years;
3. In the still-ness of the midnight, Ech-oes from the past I hear;
4. As I trav-el on life's pathway, Know not what the years may hold;

How they lin-ger, ev-er near me, And the sa-cred past un-fold.
And old home scenes of my child-hood, In fond mem - o - ry ap-pear.
Old time sing-ing, glad-ness bring-ing, From that love-ly land some-where.
As I pon-der, hope grows fon-der, Pre-cious, mem'ries flood my soul.

D. S.—In the still - ness of the mid-night, Pre-cious, sa-cred scenes un - fold.

Chorus

Pre-cious mem'ries, how they lin-ger, How they ev - er flood my soul,

116. Jesus, I Come

W. T. Sleeper
Geo. C. Stebbins

1. Out of my bond-age, sor-row and night, Je-sus, I come, Je-sus, I come;
2. Out of my shame-ful fail-ure and loss, Je-sus, I come, Je-sus, I come;
3. Out of un-rest and ar-ro-gant pride, Je-sus, I come, Je-sus, I come;
4. Out of the fear and dread of the tomb, Je-sus, I come, Je-sus, I come;

In-to Thy free-dom, glad-ness and light, Je-sus, I come to Thee;
In-to the glo-rious gain of Thy cross, Je-sus, I come to Thee;
In-to Thy bless-ed will to a-bide, Je-sus, I come to Thee;
In-to the joy and light of Thy home, Je-sus, I come to Thee;

Out of my sick-ness in-to Thy health, Out of my want and in-to Thy wealth,
Out of earth's sorrows in-to Thy balm, Out of life's storms and in-to Thy calm,
Out of my-self to dwell in Thy love, Out of de-spair in-to rap-tures a-bove,
Out of the depths of ru-in un-told, In-to the peace of Thy sheltering fold,

Out of my sin and in-to Thy-self, Je-sus, I come to Thee.
Out of dis-tress to ju-bi-lant psalm, Je-sus, I come to Thee.
Up-ward for aye on wings like a dove, Je-sus, I come to Thee.
Ev-er Thy glo-rious face to be-hold, Je-sus, I come to Thee.

Copyright, 1914, by Geo. C. Stebbins. Renewal. Hope Publishing Company, owner

No. 117 HIS WAY WITH THEE

C. S. G. Ps. 37:5. Rev. Cyrus S. Nusbaum.

1. Would you live for Jesus, and be always pure and good? Would you walk with Him with-in the nar-row road? Would you have Him bear your bur-den, car-ry all your load? Let Him have His way with thee.
2. Would you have Him make you free, and fol-low at His call? Would you know the peace that comes by giv-ing all? Would you have Him save you, so that you need nev-er fall? Let Him have His way with thee.
3. Would you in His kingdom find a place of con-stant rest? Would you prove Him true each prov-i-den-tial test? Would you in His ser-vice la-bor al-ways at your best? Let Him have His way with thee.

CHORUS.

His pow'r can make you what you ought to be; His blood can cleanse your heart and make you free; His love can fill your soul, and you will see 'Twas best for Him to have His way with thee.

Copyright, 1899, by H. L. Gilmour, Wenonah, N. J., By per.

118   I Won't Have to Cross Jordan Alone

To my friend V. O. Stamps—C. E. D.

Copyright, 1934, by The Stamps-Baxter Music Co., in "Leading Light"
Robt. H. Coleman, owner

Thomas Ramsey   **Chas. E. Durham**

May be used as a Solo

1. When I come to the riv-er at end-ing of day, When the last winds of sor-row have blown;.... There'll be some-bod-y wait-ing to show me the way, I won't have to cross Jor-dan a-lone.
2. Oft-en-times I'm for-sak-en, and wea-ry and sad, When it seems that my friends have all gone;..... There is one tho't that cheers me and makes my heart glad, I won't have to cross Jor-dan a-lone.
3. Tho the bil-lows of sor-row and trouble may sweep, Christ the Savior will care for His own;..... Till the end of the jour-ney, my soul He will keep, I won't have to cross Jor-dan a-lone.

Chorus

I won't have to cross Jor-dan a-lone, .. Je-sus died all my sins to a-tone; When the darkness I see, He'll be waiting for me, I won't have to cross Jordan alone.

Solo ad lib.   *Parts*

Hum...... Hum......

No. 119 Alone With God.

Copyright, 1904, by Wm. J. Kirkpatrick.

Rev. Johnson Oatman, Jr.   Wm. J. Kirkpatrick.

1. When storms of life are round me beating, When rough the path that I have trod,
2. What tho' the clouds have gathered o'er me? What tho' I've passed beneath the rod?
3. 'Tis there I find new strength for duty As o'er the sands of time I plod,
4. And when I see the mo-ment near-ing When I shall sleep beneath the sod,

With-in my clos-et door re-treat-ing, I love to be a-lone with God.
God's perfect will there lies before me, When I am thus a-lone with God.
I see the King in all His beau-ty, While resting there a-lone with God.
When time with me is dis-ap-pear-ing, I want to be a-lone with God.

Chorus.

A-lone with God, the world for-bid-den, A-lone with God,
A-lone with God,

O blest re-treat! A-lone with God, and in Him hid-den, To hold with Him com-munion sweet.
Alone with God,   Alone with God,   To hold with Him

No. 120   IT CLEANSETH ME

1 John 1:9
Copyright, 1899, by A. F. Myers

Rev. F. L. Snyder   A. F. Myers

1. There is a stream that flows from Cal-va-ry, A crim-son tide so deep and wide; It wash-es whit-er than the pur-est snow, It cleans-eth me, I know.
2. Its sav-ing vir-tues ev-er are the same, It cleans-eth still, and al-ways will; Poor sin-ners, who will seek the Sav-ior's face, Shall know His won-drous grace.
3. No oth-er foun-tain can for sin a-tone But Jesus' blood, O pre-cious flood! And who-so-ev-er will may plunge there-in, And be made free from sin.

CHORUS.

Hal-le-lu-jah! 'tis His blood that cleanseth me, 'Tis His grace that makes me free, And, my brother, 'tis for thee; O hal-le-lu-jah! 'tis sal-va-tion, full and free, And it cleans-eth, yes, it cleans-eth me.

No. 121 Tidings.

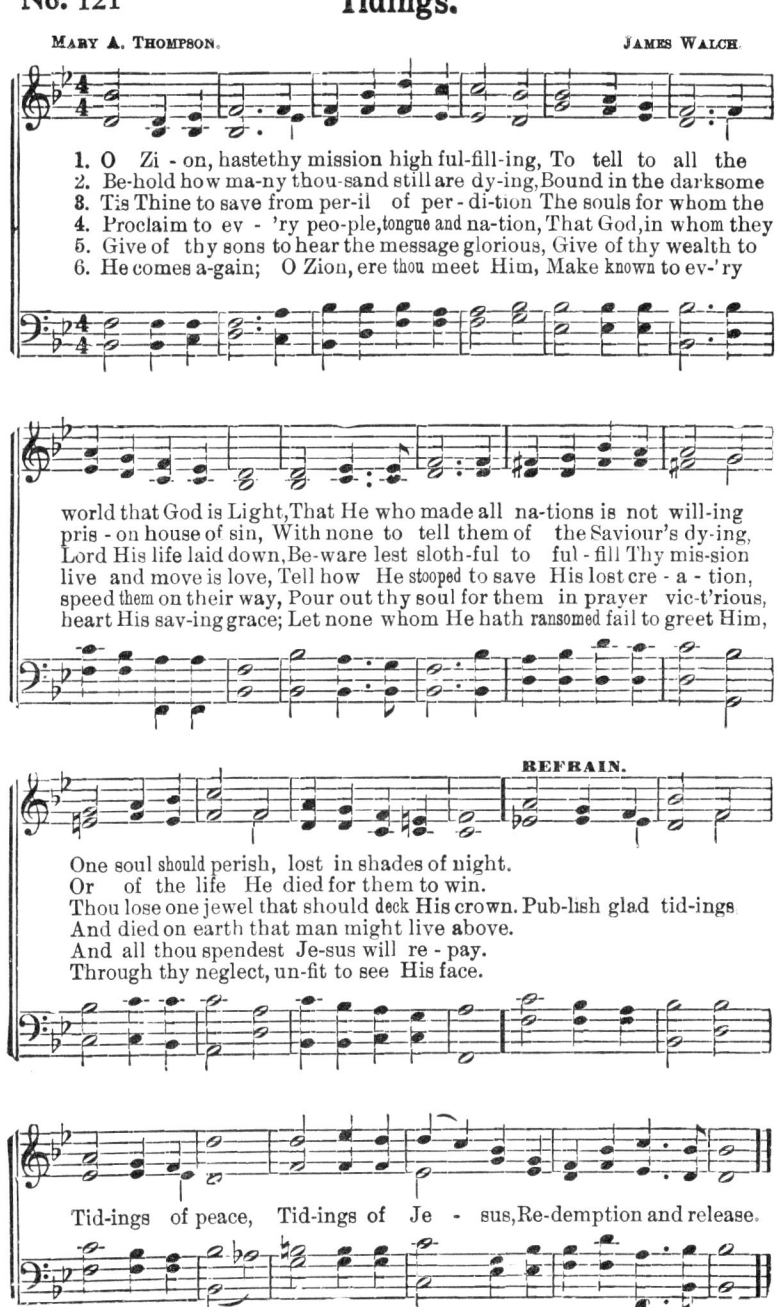

MARY A. THOMPSON. JAMES WALCH.

1. O Zi-on, haste thy mission high ful-fill-ing, To tell to all the world that God is Light, That He who made all na-tions is not will-ing One soul should perish, lost in shades of night.
2. Be-hold how ma-ny thou-sand still are dy-ing, Bound in the darksome pris-on house of sin, With none to tell them of the Saviour's dy-ing, Or of the life He died for them to win.
3. Tis Thine to save from per-il of per-di-tion The souls for whom the Lord His life laid down, Be-ware lest sloth-ful to ful-fill Thy mis-sion Thou lose one jewel that should deck His crown. Pub-lish glad tid-ings
4. Proclaim to ev-'ry peo-ple, tongue and na-tion, That God, in whom they live and move is love, Tell how He stooped to save His lost cre-a-tion, And died on earth that man might live above.
5. Give of thy sons to bear the message glorious, Give of thy wealth to speed them on their way, Pour out thy soul for them in prayer vic-t'rious And all thou spendest Je-sus will re-pay.
6. He comes a-gain; O Zion, ere thou meet Him, Make known to ev-'ry heart His sav-ing grace; Let none whom He hath ransomed fail to greet Him, Through thy neglect, un-fit to see His face.

REFRAIN.

Tid-ings of peace, Tid-ings of Je-sus, Re-demption and release.

122. Love-Light All the Way

John T. Benson, Jr., Owner
James Rowe. Copyright renewal, 1944, in "Full of Blessing No. 3." Wm. Edie Marks

1. Since I prayed that Jesus my guide would be, I have never cared to stray; For He holds my hand, and that I might see, There is love-light all the way.
2. Thro' the vales of life may my pathway lead, Where the sunbeams never play, There will still be light for my present need, There is love-light all the way.
3. Up the rugged hill, over deserts wild, I may safely go today, For the Lord is near and to light His child, There is love-light all the way.
4. Soul in darkness deep, let a change be made, Follow Jesus while you may, For with this dear Friend always near to aid, There is love-light all the way.

CHORUS.

There is love-light, Precious love-light, love-light all the way, Shining brightly night and day, Never dark for me will the home-path be; There is love-light all the way.

123. The Rock That Is Higher Than I

E. Johnson *Wm. G. Fischer*

1. O sometimes the shadows are deep, And rough seems the path to the goal,
2. O sometimes how long seems the day, And sometimes how wear-y my feet;
3. O near to the Rock let me keep, If bless-ings or sor-rows pre-vail;

And sor-rows, sometimes how they sweep Like tempests down o-ver the soul.
But toil-ing in life's dust-y way, The Rock's blessed shadow, how sweet!
Or climb-ing the mountain way steep, Or walk-ing the shad-ow-y vale.

REFRAIN.

O then to the Rock let me fly, (let me fly,) To the Rock that is high-er than I; is high-er than I; O, then to the Rock let me fly, (let me fly,) To the Rock that is high-er than I.

No. 124 Seeking the Lost.

W. A. O.
W. A. OGDEN.

1. Seek-ing the lost, yes, kind-ly en-treat-ing Wanderers on the mountain a-stray,
"Come un-to me," His message re-peat-ing, Words of the Master speaking to-day.
2. Seek-ing the lost, and pointing to Je-sus Souls that are weak and hearts that are sore,
Lead-ing them forth in ways of sal-va-tion, Showing the path to life ev-er-more.
3. Thus I would go on missions of mer-cy, Following Christ from day un-to day,
Cheer-ing the faint, and raising the fall-en, Pointing the lost to Je-sus, the Way.

CHORUS.

Go-ing a-far up-on the mountain, Bringing the wand'rer back a-gain, back a-gain In-to the fold of my Redeemer, Jesus the Lamb for sinners slain, for sinners slain.

Go-ing a-far......... up-on the mountain...... Bringing the wan - - d'rer back a-gain.......... In-to the fold........ of my Re-deem-er...... Je-sus, the Lamb,........ for sinners slain..........

No. 125 Wonderful Love.

"Behold, what manner of love the Father hath bestowed upon us."—1 John 3: 1.

May the Holy Spirit attend in mighty power the singing of this song; let no one copyright, freely let it be used to the glory of God.—Jas. H. Y.

Arranged by Cousin Eva.

1. I'm tell-ing of Je-sus, so loving and true, I'm telling His won-der-ful love,
2. I'll tell of His pardon, so gracious to me, I'll tell of His won-der-ful love,
3. I'm shouting sal-va-tion, so mighty indeed, I'm shouting His wonderful love,
4. Oh! praise Him for power His children to keep, Oh! glory for heaven's pure love;
5. I'll shout it, and sing it, His, never to roam, Sanctified, and kept by His love,
6. With Je-sus in heaven, I'll sing it a-bove, Hal-le-lu-jah, a-men and amen.

That precious old story, that ev-er is new, I'm praising His won-der-ful love.
Oh! Je-sus my Savior, has made me so free, I'm praising His won-der-ful love.
A balm for each heartache, a Friend in my need, Is Je-sus, my Sav-ior and love.
To keep us when waking and guard us in sleep, Hal-le-lu-jah for wonderful love.
I'm looking for Je-sus, so quickly to come, Oh glo-ry! Thou Heavenly Dove.
In glo-ry I'll shout it, oh wonderful love, Hal-le-lu-jah, a-men and amen.

CHORUS.

Oh! tell of His wonderful, wonderful love, There's nothing so freely He gave;

Oh! shout the glad tidings, of wonderful love, His wonderful pow-er to save.

Words and Music by Jas. H. Yeaman, Nashville, Tenn., 1904. Not copyrighted.

No. 126   **Wonderful Story of Love.**

J. M. D.   Rev. J. M. Driver. By per.

1. Won-der-ful sto-ry of love; Tell it to me a-gain;
2. Won-der-ful sto-ry of love; Tho' you are far a-way;
3. Won-der-ful sto-ry of love; Je-sus pro-vides a rest;

Won-der-ful sto-ry of love; Wake the im-mor-tal strain!
Won-der-ful sto-ry of love; Still He doth call to-day;
Won-der-ful sto-ry of love; For all the pure and blest,

An-gels with rapture announce it, Shepherds with won-der re-ceive it;
Call-ing from Cal-va-ry's mountain, Down from the crys-tal bright fountain,
Rest in those mansions a-bove us, With those who'vo gone on be-fore us,

Sin-ner, O won't you be-lieve it? Won-der-ful sto-ry of love.
E'en from the dawn of cre-a-tion, Won-der-ful sto-ry of love.
Sing-ing the rap-tur-ous cho-rus, Won-der-ful sto-ry of love.

D.S.—*Won-der-ful sto-ry of love!*

Chorus.   D.S.

Won - der - ful! Won - der - ful! Won - der - ful!
Wonderful story of love; Wonderful sto-ry of love; Wonderful sto-ry of love.

127. 'Neath the Old Olive Trees

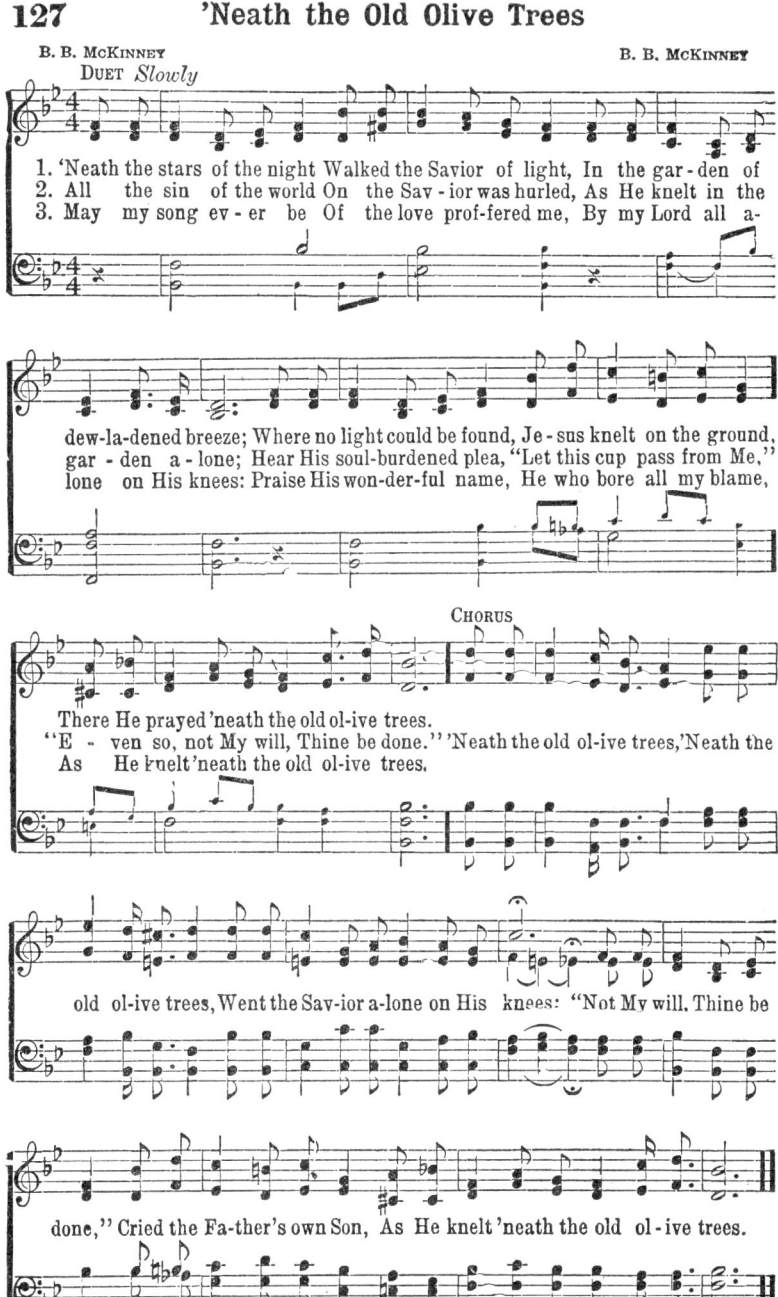

B. B. McKinney

1. 'Neath the stars of the night Walked the Savior of light, In the gar-den of dew-la-dened breeze; Where no light could be found, Je-sus knelt on the ground, There He prayed 'neath the old ol-ive trees.
2. All the sin of the world On the Sav-ior was hurled, As He knelt in the gar-den a-lone; Hear His soul-burdened plea, "Let this cup pass from Me," "E-ven so, not My will, Thine be done."
3. May my song ev-er be Of the love prof-fered me, By my Lord all a-lone on His knees: Praise His won-der-ful name, He who bore all my blame, As He knelt 'neath the old ol-ive trees.

Chorus

'Neath the old ol-ive trees, 'Neath the old ol-ive trees, Went the Sav-ior a-lone on His knees: "Not My will, Thine be done," Cried the Fa-ther's own Son, As He knelt 'neath the old ol-ive trees.

Copyright, 1929, by Robert H. Coleman. International Copyright secured. Used by permission

No. 128. Come Unto Me

E. E. Hewitt
D. Ward Milam

1. Come, all ye wear-y and oppressed, O come and I will give you rest;
I'll bid your anx-ious fears de-part, For I am meek and low-ly in heart,
For I am meek and low-ly in heart,

2. Come, ye that feel the weight of sin, And I will breathe sweet peace within;
I'll lift the bur-den from your heart, Forgiveness I will free-ly im-part,
For-give-ness I will free-ly im-part, And I will give you rest.

3. So ten-der-ly my Sav-iour pleads, For all His own He in-ter-cedes,
And still He's call-ing, Come to me, And ye shall find rest un-to your soul,
For I am meek and low-ly in heart,

CHORUS.

Ye that la-bor and are heav-y la-den, come to Me, (to Me,)
Come, come, come,.......... and learn of Me;
Take My yoke, My yoke up-on you, and learn, and learn of Me, of Me;

Come Unto Me - concluded -

My yoke is eas-y, My bur-den is light, My yoke is eas-y, My bur-den is light, Come, come, Come and I will give you rest.

For my yoke is eas-y, and My bur-den is light, My bur-den is light, For My yoke is eas-y and My bur-den is light, My bur-den is light, Come, O come,

For my yoke is eas-y, My bur-den is

No. 129. All Hail the Power

Edward Perronet
William Shrubsole

1. All hail the pow'r of Je-sus' name! Let angels prostrate fall; Bring forth the roy-al di-a-dem,
2. Ye chosen seed of Is-ra-el's race, Ye ransomed from the fall; Hail Him who saves you by His grace, And crown Him, crown Him, crown Him, Crown Him Lord of all.
3. O that with yonder sa-cred throng, We at His feet may fall; We'll join the ev-er-last-ing song,

No. 130 HALLELUJAH! PRAISE JEHOVAH

By permission of Hope Pub. Co.

Psalm 16
Wm. J. Kirkpatrick

1. Hal - le - lu - jah, praise Je - ho - vah! From the heav-ens praise His name;
2. Let them prais-es give Je - ho - vah, They were made at His com-mand;
3. All ye fruit-ful trees and ce - dars, All ye hills and moun-tains high,

Praise Je - ho - vah in the high - est, All His an - gels praise pro-claim.
Them for - ev - er He es - tab-lished, His de - cree shall ev - er stand.
Creep-ing things and beasts and cat - tle, Birds that in the heav-ens fly.

All His hosts to - geth - er praise Him, Sun, and moon, and stars on high;
From the earth, O praise Je - ho - vah, All ye floods, ye drag - ons all;
Kings of earth and all ye peo - ple, Princ-es great, earth's judg-es all;

Praise Him, O ye heav'n of heav - ens, And ye floods a - bove the sky.
Fire, and hail, and snow, and va - pors, Storm-y winds that hear Him call.
Praise His name, young men and maid - ens, A - ged men, and chil-dren small.

Chorus

Let them prais - es give Je - ho - vah, For His name a - lone is high,
Let them prais - es

HALLELUJAH, PRAISE JEHOVAH—Concluded

And His glo - ry is ex - alt - ed, And His glo - ry is ex - alt - ed,
And His glo - ry And His glo - ry
And His glo - ry is ex - alt - ed Far a-bove the earth and sky.
And His glo - ry

No. 131 TAKE MY LIFE AND LET IT BE

Frances R. Havergal Abraham H. C. Malan

1. Take my life, and let it be Con - se - crat - ed, Lord, to Thee; Take my hands, and let them move At the im - pulse of Thy love, At the im - pulse of Thy love.
2. Take my feet, and let them be Swift and beau - ti - ful for Thee; Take my voice, and let me sing Al - ways, on - ly, for my King, Al - ways, on - ly, for my King.
3. Take my lips, and let them be Filled with mes - sag - es from Thee; Take my sil - ver and my gold, Not a mite would I with - hold, Not a mite would I with - hold.
4. Take my will and make it Thine; It shall be no lon - ger mine; Take my heart, it is Thine own! It shall be Thy roy - al throne, It shall be Thy roy - al throne.
5. Take my love; my Lord, I pour At Thy feet its treas-ure-store; Take my - self, and I will be, Ev - er, on - ly, all for Thee, Ev - er, on - ly, all for Thee.

132. Wonderful Grace of Jesus

Copyright Renewal, 1946 by Haldor Lillenas
Hope Publishing Co, Owner

H. L.
Haldor Lillenas

1. Won-der-ful grace of Je-sus, Great-er than all my sin;
2. Won-der-ful grace of Je-sus, Reach-ing to all the lost,
3. Won-der-ful grace of Je-sus, Reach-ing the most de-filed,

How shall my tongue de-scribe it, Where shall His praise be-gin?
By it I have been par-doned, Saved to the ut-ter-most;
By its trans-form-ing pow-er, Mak-ing him God's dear child,

Tak-ing a-way my bur-den, Set-ting my spir-it free;
Chains have been torn a-sun-der, Giv-ing me lib-er-ty;
Pur-chas-ing peace and heav-en, For all e-ter-ni-ty;

For the won-der-ful grace of Je-sus reach-es me.
For the won-der-ful grace of Je-sus reach-es me.
And the won-der-ful grace of Je-sus reach-es me.

Chorus

Won-der-ful the match-less grace of Je - - - sus, the match-less grace of Je-sus,

Wonderful Grace of Jesus

Deep - er than the might-y roll - ing sea; the roll - ing sea;

Won - der - ful grace, all - suf - fi -
High-er than the moun-tain, spar-kling like a foun - tain, All - suf - fi - cient

cient for me, for e - ven me, Broad-er than the scope of my trans-
grace for e - ven me,

gres - sions, Great-er far than all my sin and shame,
gres-sions, sing it! my sin and shame,

O mag - ni - fy the pre - cious name of Je - sus, Praise His name!

134. Jesus Paid It All

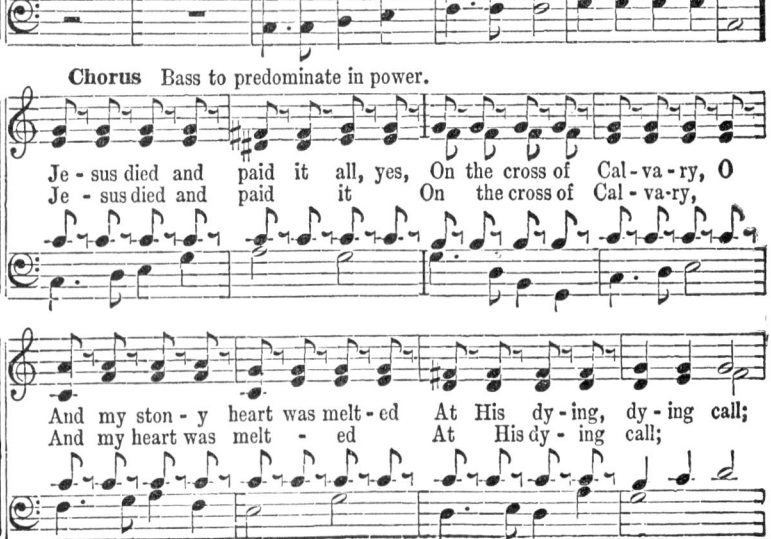

Copyright, 1944, Renewal. Stamps-Baxter Music & Ptg. Co., owners

M. S. Shaffer
Samuel W. Beazley

1. Gone is all my debt of sin, A great change is bro't within, And to live I now be-gin, Ris-en from the fall; Yet the debt I did not pay, Some One died for me one day, Sweeping all the debt a-way, Je-sus paid it all.

2. O I hope to please Him now, Light of joy is on my brow, As at His dear feet I bow, Safe with-in His love; Mak-ing His the debt I owed, Free-dom true He has bestowed: So I'm sing-ing on the road To my home a-bove.

3. Sin-ner, not for me a-lone Did the Son of God a-tone; Your debt, too, He made His own, On the cru-el tree; Come to Him with all your sin, Be as white as snow with-in; Full sal-va-tion you may win And re-joice with me.

Chorus Bass to predominate in power.

Je-sus died and paid it all, yes, On the cross of Cal-va-ry, O
Je-sus died and paid it On the cross of Cal-va-ry,
And my ston-y heart was melt-ed At His dy-ing, dy-ing call;
And my heart was melt - ed At His dy-ing call;

Jesus Paid It All

O His heart in shame was brok-en On the tree for you and me, yes,
O His heart was brok - en On the tree for you and me,

And the debt, the debt is can-celled, Je - sus paid it, paid it all.
And the debt is can - celled, Je - sus paid it all.

135 What Did He Do?

Anon. alt.
W. Owen

1. O lis-ten to our wondrous sto - ry: Once we dwelt a-mong the lost,
   Yet Je-sus came from heaven's glo - ry, Sav-ing us at aw-ful cost,
2. No an-gel could our place have tak - en, High-est of the high tho He,
   Nailed to the cross, despised, forsak - en, Was one of the God-head three!
3. Will you sur-ren-der to this Sav - ior? Now be-fore Him hum-bly bow,
   You, too, shall come to know His fa - vor, He will save and save you now.

Chorus

Who saved us from e - ter-nal loss? What did He do?
Who but God's Son up-on the cross! He

Where is He now? In heav - en in - ter - ced - ing!
died for you! Be-lieve it thou, In

No. 136　　　　　　　　There Is a Fountain

As sung by Miss Essie Morris and
Mrs. Winifred Carroll.

Arr. by Mrs. Jno. T. Benson.

DUET.

1. There is a foun - - tain filled with blood,　Drawn from Immanuel's veins,......... And sinners, plunged........ be - neath that flood, Loose all...... their guilt-y stains.
2. The dy-ing thief........... re-joiced to see　That foun - tain in his day,........... And there may I............. tho' vile as he, Wash all...... my sins a - way.
3. E'er since by faith........... I saw the stream　Thy flow - ing wounds supply,......... Re-deem-ing love............ has been my theme, And shall.... be till I die.
4. Then in a no - - bler, sweet-er song　I'll sing.... Thy pow'r to save,......... When this poor, lisp - ing, stamm'ring tongue Lies si - - lent in the grave.

1. There is a foun-tain, filled with blood, Drawn from Immanuel's veins, And sinners, plunged be-neath that flood,

CHORUS.

I've been redeemed (and so have I), I've been redeemed (and so have I), I've been redeemed (and so have I), I've been redeemed (and so have I), I've been washed in the blood of the

Copyright Renewal, 1940, John T. Benson, Jr., Owner.

There Is a Fountain (Concluded)

Lamb, I've been washed in the blood of the
Hal - le - lu - jah,

Lamb, I've been washed in the blood of the
Praise the Lord,

Lamb, that flows from Cal - va - ry.
Hal - le - lu - jah, from Cal - va - ry.

No. 137 **THERE IS A FOUNTAIN.**

WM. COWPER. Western Melody.

1. There is a fountain fill'd with blood, Drawn from Immanuel's veins, And sinners, plung'd beneath that flood,
2. The dying thief rejoiced to see That fountain in his day, And there may I, tho' vile as he,
3. E'er since by faith I saw the stream Thy flowing wounds supply, Redeeming love has been my theme,
4. Then in a nobler, sweeter song I'll sing Thy pow'r to save, When this poor, lisping, stamm'ring tongue

FINE. D. S.

Lose all their guilty stains, Lose all their guilty stains, Lose all their guilty stains.
Wash all my sins a - way, Wash all my sins a - way, Wash all my sins a - way.
And shall be till I die, And shall be till I die, And shall be till I die.
Lies si - lent in the grave, Lies si - lent in the grave, Lies si - lent in the grave,

No. 138 Master the Tempest Is Raging

H. R. Palmer

1. Mas-ter, the tempest is rag-ing! The bil-lows are toss-ing high!
2. Mas-ter, with an-guish of spir-it I bow in my grief to-day;
3. Mas-ter, the ter-ror is o-ver, The el-e-ments sweet-ly rest;

The sky is o'er-shadowed with black-ness, No shel-ter or help is nigh;
The depths of my sad heart are troub-led—Oh wak-eh and save, I pray!
Earth's sun in the calm lake is mir-rored, And heaven's with-in my breast;

Car-est Thou not that we per-ish? How canst Thou lie a-sleep;
Tor-rents of sin and of an-guish Sweep o'er my sink-ing soul;
Lin-ger, O bless-ed Re-deem-er! Leave me a-lone no more;

When each moment so mad-ly is threat'ning A grave in the an-gry deep?
And I per-ish! I per-ish! dear Mas-ter—Oh has-ten, and take con-trol.
And with joy I shall make the best har-bor, And rest on the bliss-ful shore.

CHORUS.

The winds and the waves shall o-bey Thy will, Peace be still!
Peace, be still! peace, be still!

Master the Tempest Is Raging

Wheth-er the wrath of the storm-tossed sea, Or de-mons or men, or what ev-er it be, No wa-ters can swal-low the ship where lies The Mas-ter of o-cean, and earth, and skies; They all shall sweet-ly o-bey Thy will, Peace, be still! Peace be still! They all shall sweet-ly o-bey Thy will, Peace, peace, be still!

No. 139   HE'LL TAKE YOU THROUGH

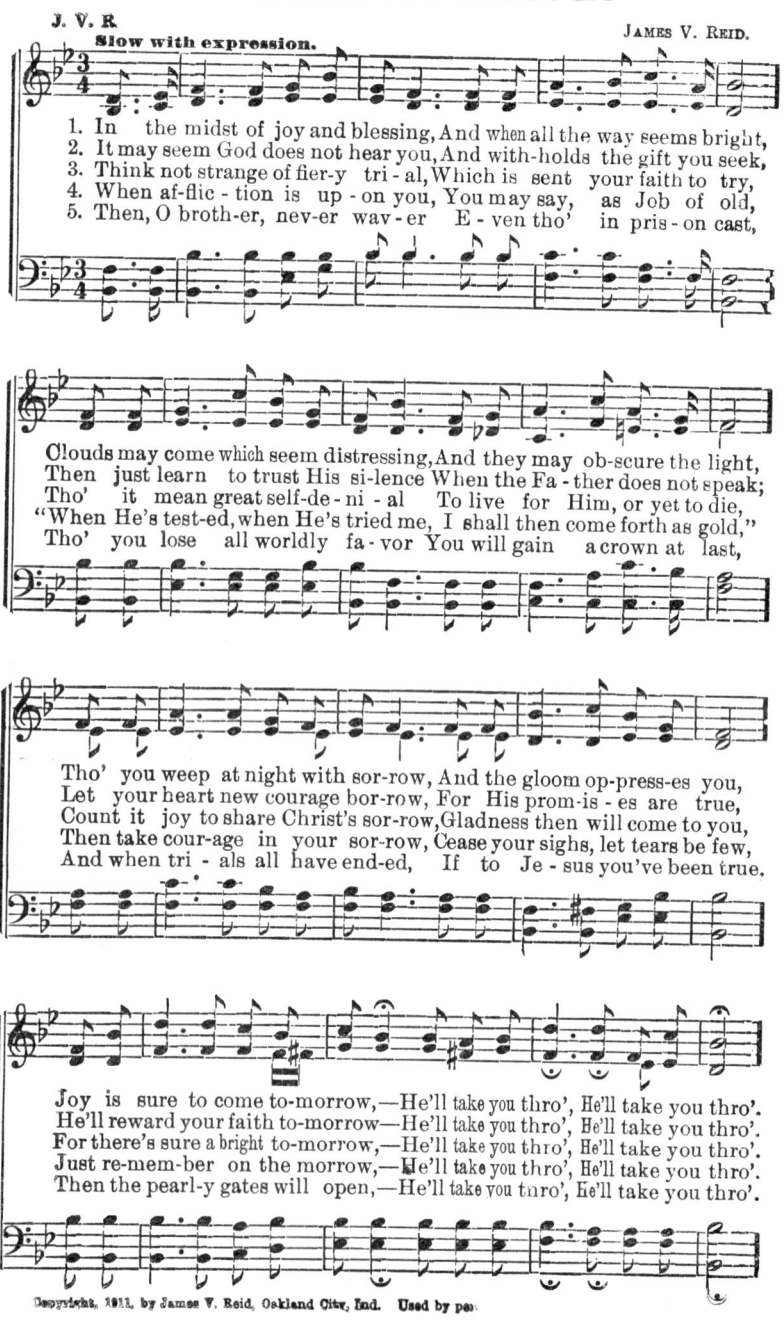

J. V. R.   James V. Reid.

Slow with expression.

1. In the midst of joy and blessing, And when all the way seems bright,
2. It may seem God does not hear you, And with-holds the gift you seek,
3. Think not strange of fier-y tri-al, Which is sent your faith to try,
4. When af-flic-tion is up-on you, You may say, as Job of old,
5. Then, O broth-er, nev-er wav-er E-ven tho' in pris-on cast,

Clouds may come which seem distressing, And they may ob-scure the light,
Then just learn to trust His si-lence When the Fa-ther does not speak;
Tho' it mean great self-de-ni-al To live for Him, or yet to die,
"When He's test-ed, when He's tried me, I shall then come forth as gold,"
Tho' you lose all worldly fa-vor You will gain a crown at last,

Tho' you weep at night with sor-row, And the gloom op-press-es you,
Let your heart new courage bor-row, For His prom-is-es are true,
Count it joy to share Christ's sor-row, Gladness then will come to you,
Then take cour-age in your sor-row, Cease your sighs, let tears be few,
And when tri-als all have end-ed, If to Je-sus you've been true.

Joy is sure to come to-morrow,—He'll take you thro', He'll take you thro'.
He'll reward your faith to-morrow—He'll take you thro', He'll take you thro'.
For there's sure a bright to-morrow,—He'll take you thro', He'll take you thro'.
Just re-mem-ber on the morrow,—He'll take you thro', He'll take you thro'.
Then the pearl-y gates will open,—He'll take you thro', He'll take you thro'.

Copyright, 1911, by James V. Reid, Oakland City, Ind. Used by per.

HE'LL TAKE YOU THROUGH (Concluded)

He'll take you thro',.......... How-ev-er you're tried;..........
He'll take you thro', How-ev-er you're tried;

His ten-der care............ is nev-er de-nied............
His ten-der care is ne'er de-nied,

Then al-ways trust............ His promise so true............
Then al-ways trust His promise so true,

rit.

He'll take you thro',.... ...... He'll take you thro'............
He'll take you thro', He'll take you thro

No. 140 Christ is King.

Chas. Reign Scoville.
Copyright, 1933. Renewal by De Loss Smith.
The Standard Pub. Co., Owners.
De Loss Smith.

1. Come friends sing, of the faith that's so dear to me,
2. Cru - ci - fied, thus He suf - fered and bled for me,
3. At His feet, on old Ol - i - vet's Hill they say,

Re - vealed thro' God's Son, in Gai - i - lee; He brought
Death and the grave won sin's vic - to - ry; Then the
Cloud char - iots halt - ed, took Christ a - way; Then the

peace on earth and good will to the sons of men,
sky grew dark and the tem - ple veil rent in twain,
an - gels came and to wond'ring dis - ci - ples said

Go tell it to the world, her King reigns a - gain.
Rocks rent, and an - gels came, for He lived a - gain.
He'll come, and earth and sea shall yield up their dead.

Christ is King.

CHORUS.

I am so hap-py in Je-sus, Cap-tiv-i-ty's Cap-tor is He;... An-gels re-joice when a souls saved, Some day we like Him shall be,... Sor-row and joy have the same Lord, Val-ley of shadows shall sing;... Death has its life, its door o-pens in heav-en e-ter-nal-ly, Christ is King...

No. 141   AWAKENING CHORUS

Charlotte G. Homer   *Chas. H. Gabriel*

1. A-wake! A-wake! a-wake! a-wake! and sing the bless-ed sto-ry; A-wake! A-wake! a-wake! a-wake! and let your song of praise a-rise; A-wake! A-wake! a-wake! the earth is full of glo-ry, And light is And light beam-ing from the ra-diant skies; The rocks and rills, the vales and hills re-sound with glad-ness, All na-ture joins to sing the tri-umph

2. Ring out! Ring out! ring out! ring out! O bells of joy and glad-ness! Re-peat, Re-peat, re-peat re-peat a-new the sto-ry o'er a-gain, Till all Till all the earth the earth shall lose its weight of sad-ness, And shout a-new a-new the glo-ri-ous re-frain; With an-gels in the heights sing-ing of the great sal-va-tion He wrest-ed from the hand of sin and

Male voices in Unison

Copyrighted 1933. Renewal, The Rodeheaver Company, Owner.

AWAKENING CHORUS

song. The Lord Je-ho-vah reigns and sin is back-ward hurled!
death. The Lord Je-ho-vah reigns and sin is back-ward hurled!
sin is backward hurled!

Unison
Re-joice, re-joice! Lift heart and voice; Je-ho-vah reigns!

Full harmony
Pro-claim His sov-'reign pow'r to all the world, And let His
pow'r to all the world, And let the

glo - rious ban-ner be un-furled! Je-ho-vah reigns!
grand and glo-rious ban-ner be un-furled! Je-ho-vah reigns! Je-ho-vah reigns!

Re-joice! re - joice! re-joice! Je-ho-vah reigns!
Re-joice! re - joice! re-joice!

142. Hallelujah For the Cross!

HORATIUS BONAR, arr.
JAMES McGRANAHAN

1. The cross it stand-eth fast, Hal-le-lu-jah, hal-le-lu-jah! De-fy-ing ev-'ry blast, Hal-le-lu-jah, hal-le-lu-jah! The winds of hell have blown, The world its hate hath shown, Yet it is not o-ver-thrown, Hal-le-lu-jah for the cross!

2. It is the old cross still, Hal-le-lu-jah, hal-le-lu-jah! Its tri-umph let us tell, Hal-le-lu-jah, hal-le-lu-jah! The grace of God here shone Thro' Christ the bless-ed Son, Who did for sin a-tone, Hal-le-lu-jah for the cross!

3. 'Twas here the debt was paid, Hal-le-lu-jah, hal-le-lu-jah! Our sins on Je-sus laid, Hal-le-lu-jah, hal-le-lu-jah! So round the cross we sing Of Christ our of-fer-ing, Of Christ our liv-ing King, Hal-le-lu-jah for the cross!

OBBLIGATO DUET Sop. (or Ten.) and Alto
Hal-le-lu-jah, hal-le-lu-jah, hal-le-

Soprano and Alto*

CHORUS *mp.* Hal-le-lu-jah hal-le-lu-jah, hal-le-

Tenor and Bass

*If desired, the Soprano and Alto may sing the upper staff, omitting the middle staff.

Hallelujah For the Cross!

lu - - jah for the cross! Hal - le - lu - jah, hal - le - lu - jah, It shall nev - er suf - fer loss!

lu - jah for the cross, hal-le-lu - jah for the cross! Hal - le - lu - jah, hal - le - lu - jah, It shall nev - er suf - fer, nev - er suf - fer loss!

Full Chorus
*Hal - le - lu - jah, hal - le - lu - jah, hal - le - lu - jah for the cross! Hal - le - lu - jah, hal - le - lu - jah, It shall nev - er suf - fer loss!

*For a final ending, all the voices may sing the melody in unison through the last eight measures—the instrument playing the harmony.

No. 143   **All Hail, Immanuel!**

D. R. Van Sickle.   Chas. H. Gabriel.

1. All hail to Thee, Im-man-u-el, We cast........our crowns be-fore Thee; Let ev-'ry heart o-bey Thy will, And ev- - -'ry voice a-round Thee. In praise to Thee, our Sav-ior, King, The vi-brant chords of heav-en ring, And ech-o back the might-y strain: All hail! all hail! All hail, all hail, Im-man-u-el!

2. All hail to Thee, Im-man-u-el, The ran- - -somed hosts sur-round Thee; And earthly monarchs clamor forth Their Sov- -'reign, King to crown Thee. While those redeemed in a-ges gone, As-sem-bled round the great white throne, Break forth in-to im-mor-tal song: All hail! all hail! All hail, all hail, Im-man-u-el!

3. All hail to Thee, Im-man-u-el, Our ris- - -en King and Sav-ior! Thy foes are vanquished, and Thou art Om-nip-o-tent for-ev- -er. Death, sin and hell no lon-ger reign, And Sa-tan's pow'r is burst in twain; E-ter-nal glo-ry to Thy Name: All hail! all hail! All hail, all hail, Im-man-u-el!

Copyright Renewal, 1938—The Rodeheaver Co., Owner

All Hail, Immanuel!

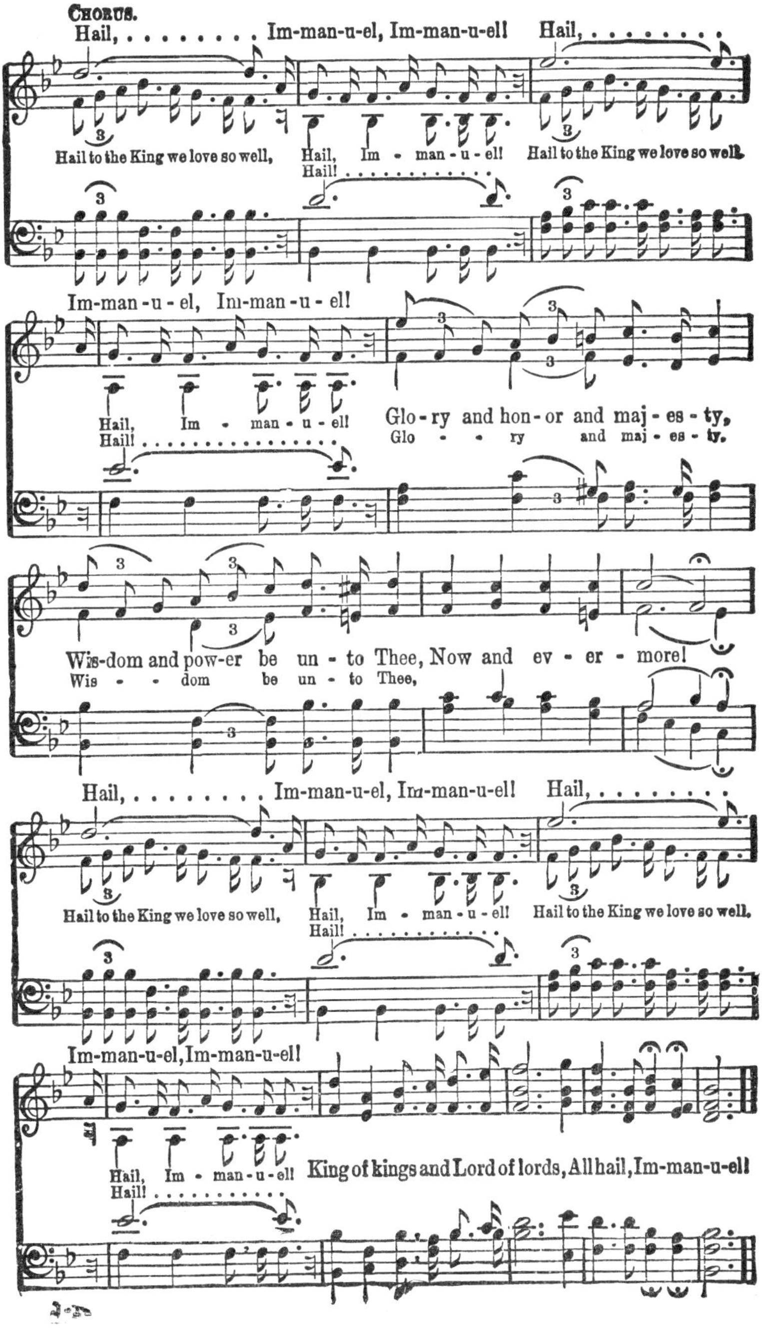

144. He is Mine.

C. Austin Miles.   J. Lincoln Hall.

1. There is a Shepherd who cares for his own, And he is mine; Nothing am I, he's a King on a throne, But he is mine; How he can love such a sinner as I, Tho' he is mine; I cannot fathom tho' oft-en I try, But he is mine.
2. Jesus left heaven my Saviour to be, And he is mine; I am not worth all he suffered for me, But he is mine; Tho' I'm not worthy he dwells in my heart, And he is mine; From him I'll never, no, never depart, For he is mine.
3. There is a Comfort-er come from above, He too is mine, Coming to me to reveal Jesus' love, And that is mine; Shepherd and Saviour, and Comforter, too, They all are mine; That's why I know the old story is true, They all are mine.

Tenor and Basses, or all in unison, or solo.

CHORUS.

He is mine, . . . He is mine; Tho' it is wonder-ful, yet it is true, That he is mine.

Tho' all un-worthy, I know he is mine, He is mine, yes, he is mine;

Copyright Renewal. 1940—The Rodeheaver Co., Owner

No. 145 Is Your All on the Altar?

E. A. H.
Rev. Elisha A. Hoffman.

1. You have longed for sweet peace, and for faith to increase, And have ear-nest-ly fer-vent-ly pray'd; But you can-not have rest, or be per-fect-ly blest Un-til all on the al-tar is laid.
2. Would you walk with the Lord, in the light of His word, And have peace and con-tentment al - way, You must do His sweet will, to be free from all ill, On the al-tar your all you must lay.
3. Oh, we nev-er can know what the Lord will be-stow Of the blessings for which we have pray'd, Till our bod-y and soul He doth ful-ly con-trol, And our all on the al-tar is laid.
4. Who can tell all the love He will send from a-bove, And how hap-py our hearts will be made, Of the fel-low-ship sweet we shall share at His feet, When our all on the al-tar is laid.

CHORUS.

Is your all on the al-tar of sac-ri-fice laid? Your heart, does the Spirit control?...... You can on-ly be blest and have peace and sweet rest, As you yield Him your bod-y and soul.

Copyright, 1900, by E. A. Hoffman.

No. 146 Are you Washed in the Blood?

"The blood of Christ cleanseth us from all sin."—1 John 1: 7.

E. A. H. E. A. HOFFMAN.

1. Have you been to Jesus for the cleansing pow'r? Are you washed in the blood of the Lamb? Are you fully trusting in His grace this hour? Are you washed in the blood of the Lamb?
2. Are you walking daily by the Saviour's side? Are you washed in the blood of the Lamb? Do you rest each moment in the Crucified? Are you washed in the blood of the Lamb?
3. When the Bridegroom cometh will your robes be white, Pure and white in the blood of the Lamb? Will your soul be ready for the mansions bright, And be washed in the blood of the Lamb?
4. Lay aside the garments that are stained with sin, And be washed in the blood of the Lamb? There's a fountain flowing for the souls unclean, O be washed in the blood of the Lamb!

CHORUS.

Are you washed in the blood, In the soul-cleansing blood of the Lamb? Are your garments spotless? Are they white as snow? Are they washed in the blood of the Lamb?

Copyright, 1879, by E. A. Hoffman.

No. 147. Who At My Door Is Standing

Mrs. M. B. C. Slade
A. B. Everett

1. Who at my door is stand-ing,— Pa-tient-ly draw-ing near,
2. Lone-ly with-out He's stay-ing: Lone-ly with-in am I.
3. All thru the dark honrs drear-y, Knock-ing a-gain is He,
4. Door of my heart, I has-ten! Thee will I o-pen wide.

En-trance with-in de-mand-ing? Whose is the voice I hear?
While I am still de-lay-ing, Will He not pass me by?
Je-sus, art Thou not wea-ry, Wait-ing so long for me?
Tho' He re-buke and chas-ten, He shall a-bide with me.

Refrain

Sweet-ly the tones are fall-ing:— "O-pen the door for me!
If thou wilt heed my call-ing, I will a-bide with thee."

No. 148. Come to Jesus

Unknown

1. Come to Je-sus, come to Je-sus,

2. He will save you.
3. He is able.
4. He is willing.
5. Call upon Him.
6. He will hear you.
7. He'll forgive you.
8. He will cleanse you.
9. Jesus loves you.
10. Only trust Him.

No. 149 — Softly and Tenderly

W. L. T.   *Will L. Thompson.*

1. Soft-ly and ten-der-ly Je-sus is call-ing, Call-ing for you and for me;
   At the heart's por-tal He's waiting and watching, Watching for you and for me.
2. Why should we tarry when Je-sus is plead-ing, Plead-ing for you and for me?
   Why should we lin-ger and heed not His mercies, Mer-cies for you and for me?
3. Time is now fleeting, the moments are pass-ing, Pass-ing from you and from me;
   Shadows are gath'ring, and death's night is coming, Com-ing for you and for me.
4. Think of the won-der-ful love He has promised, Promised for you and for me;
   Tho' we have sinn'd, He has mer-cy and par-don, Par-don for you and for me.

Chorus.

Come home, come home, Ye who are wea-ry, come home,
Ear-nest-ly, ten-der-ly, Je-sus is call-ing, Call-ing, O sin-ner, come home!

No. 150 — JUST AS I AM.

Charlotte Elliott.   *Wm. Bradbury.*

1. Just as I am! without one plea, But that Thy blood was shed for me, And that Thou bidd'st me come to Thee, O Lamb of God! I come! I come!
2. Just as I am! and waiting not To rid my soul of one dark blot, To Thee whose blood can cleanse each spot, O Lamb of God! I come! I come!
3. Just as I am! tho' toss'd about, With many a conflict, many a doubt, Fighting and fears with-in, with-out, O Lamb of God! I come! I come!
4. Just as I am! poor, wretched, blind, Sight, riches, healing of the mind, Yea, all I need in Thee to find, O Lamb of God! I come! I come!
5. Just as I am! Thou wilt receive, Wilt welcome, pardon, cleanse, relieve; Because Thy promise I believe, O Lamb of God! I come! I come!

No. 151 **Jesus is Calling.**

1. Je-sus is ten-der-ly call-ing thee home—Call-ing to-day, calling to-day;
2. Je-sus is call-ing the wear-y to rest—Call-ing to-day, calling to-day;
3. Je-sus is waiting, oh, come to Him now—Waiting to-day, waiting to-day;
4. Je-sus is pleading, oh, list to His voice—Hear Him to-day, hear Him to-day;

Why from the sun-shine of love wilt thou roam Far-ther and far-ther a-way?
Bring Him thy bur-den, and thou shalt be blest; He will not turn Thee a-way.
Come with thy sins, at His feet low-ly bow; Come, and no lon-ger de-lay.
They who be-lieve on His name shall re-joice; Quickly a-rise and a-way.

Call - ing to - day! Call - ing to - day!
Call-ing, call-ing to - day, to-day! Call-ing, call-ing to - day, to-day!

Je - sus is call - ing, is ten-der-ly call-ing to - day.
Je-sus is ten-der-ly call-ing to-day,

---

152 **Salvation in My Heart.** Arr. by R. E. W.

FINE. CHORUS. D. C.

CHO.—1. I'm glad I have salvation in my heart, in my heart. In my heart, in my heart.

Owned by R. E. Winsett. praise the Lord, Amen.

2 I have no condemnation in my heart, :||
3 I want to be like Jesus in my heart, :||
4 I will not be deceitful in my heart, :||
I'm glad I love my Saviour in my heart, :||

7 I'm glad I love my enemies in my heart, :||
8 I feel the fire a-burning in my heart, :||
9 I have the Holy Spirit in my heart, :||
10 There's glory hallelujah in my heart. :||

No. 153   WHITER THAN SNOW

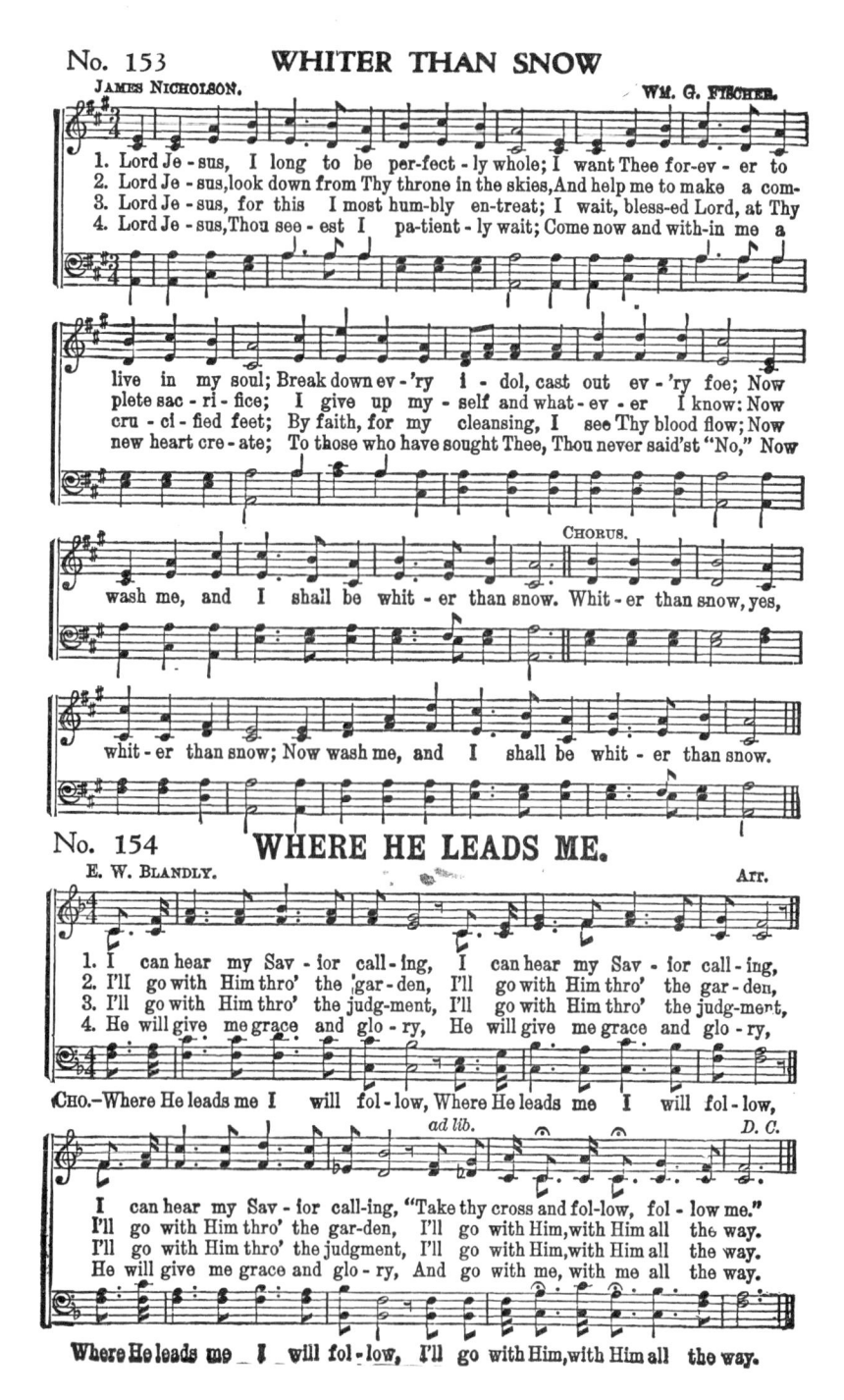

JAMES NICHOLSON.   WM. G. FISCHER.

1. Lord Je-sus, I long to be per-fect-ly whole; I want Thee for-ev-er to live in my soul; Break down ev-'ry i-dol, cast out ev-'ry foe; Now wash me, and I shall be whit-er than snow.
2. Lord Je-sus, look down from Thy throne in the skies, And help me to make a com-plete sac-ri-fice; I give up my-self and what-ev-er I know: Now wash me, and I shall be whit-er than snow.
3. Lord Je-sus, for this I most hum-bly en-treat; I wait, bless-ed Lord, at Thy cru-ci-fied feet; By faith, for my cleansing, I see Thy blood flow; Now wash me, and I shall be whit-er than snow.
4. Lord Je-sus, Thou see-est I pa-tient-ly wait; Come now and with-in me a new heart cre-ate; To those who have sought Thee, Thou never said'st "No," Now wash me, and I shall be whit-er than snow.

CHORUS.

Whit-er than snow, yes, whit-er than snow; Now wash me, and I shall be whit-er than snow.

No. 154   WHERE HE LEADS ME.

E. W. BLANDLY.   Arr.

1. I can hear my Sav-ior call-ing, I can hear my Sav-ior call-ing, I can hear my Sav-ior call-ing, "Take thy cross and fol-low, fol-low me."
2. I'll go with Him thro' the gar-den, I'll go with Him thro' the gar-den, I'll go with Him thro' the gar-den, I'll go with Him, with Him all the way.
3. I'll go with Him thro' the judg-ment, I'll go with Him thro' the judg-ment, I'll go with Him thro' the judgment, I'll go with Him, with Him all the way.
4. He will give me grace and glo-ry, He will give me grace and glo-ry, He will give me grace and glo-ry, And go with me, with me all the way.

CHO.—Where He leads me I will fol-low, Where He leads me I will fol-low, Where He leads me I will fol-low, I'll go with Him, with Him all the way.

No. 155 JESUS PAID IT ALL.

Mrs. Elvina M. Hall. John T. Grape.

1. I hear the Sav-ior say, Thy strength indeed is small; Child of weakness, watch and pray, Find in me thine all in all.
2. Lord, now in-deed I find Thy pow'r, and Thine a-lone Can change the lep-er's spots, And melt the heart of stone.
3. For noth-ing good have I Where-by Thy grace to claim— I'll wash my gar-ment white In the blood of Cal-v'ry's Lamb.
4. And when be-fore the throne I stand in Him com-plete, I'll lay my tro-phies down, All down at Je-sus' feet.

CHORUS.

Je-sus paid it all, All to Him I owe; Sin had left a crim-son stain; He washed it white as snow.

No. 156 I AM COMING, LORD.

L. H. Rev. L. Hartsough.

1. I hear Thy welcome voice, That calls me, Lord, to Thee, For cleans-ing in Thy pre-cious blood That flowed on Cal-va-ry.
2. Tho' com-ing weak and vile, Thou dost my strength assure; Thou dost my vileness ful-ly cleanse, Till spot-less all and pure.
3. 'Tis Je-sus calls me on To per-fect faith and love, To per-fect hope, and peace, and trust, For earth and heav'n a-bove.

CHORUS.

I am com-ing, Lord! Com-ing now to Thee! Wash me, cleanse me in the blood That flowed on Cal-va-ry!

No. 157   Jesus Breaks Every Fetter.

Old Melody

1. I am all on the al-tar, I am all on the al-tar,
2. He ac-cepts all I've brought Him, He ac-cepts all I've brought Him,
3. I will nev-er-more doubt Him, I will nev-er-more doubt Him,
4. I will rest on His prom-ise, I will rest on His prom-ise,
5. Hal-le-lujah! I will praise Him, Hal-le-lujah I will praise Him,

CHO.—Je-sus breaks ev-'ry fet-ter, Je-sus breaks ev-'ry fet-ter,

   I am all on the al-tar; Which was made for me.
   He ac-cepts all I've brought Him; And that's e-ven me.
   I will nev-er-more doubt Him; For He cleans-es me.
   I will rest on His prom-ise; Which was made for me.
   Ha-le-lujah! I will praise Him; For He sets me free.

Je-sus breaks ev-'ry fet-ter, Je-sus sets me free.

No. 158   The Old Time Religion.

Unknown.   E. O. E. Arr.

CHO—'Tis the old time re-lig-ion, Tis the old time re-lig-ion, 'Tis the old time re-lig-ion, And it's good enough for me.
1. It was good for our mothers, It was good for our mothers, It was good for our mothers, And it's good enough for me.

No. 159   IS THY HEART RIGHT WITH GOD?

E. A. H.   Rev. Elisha A. Hoffman.

1. Have thy af-fec-tions been nailed to the cross? Is thy heart right with God?
2. Hast thou do-min-ion o'er self and o'er sin? Is thy heart right with God?
3. Is there no more con-dem-na-tion for sin? Is thy heart right with God?
4. Art thou now walking in heav-en's pure light? Is thy heart right with God?

Countest thou all things for Je-sus but loss? Is thy heart right with God?
O-ver all e-vil with-out and with-in? Is thy heart right with God?
Does Je-sus rule in the tem-ple with-in? Is thy heart right with God?
Is thy soul wearing the gar-ment of white? Is thy heart right with God?

IS THY HEART RIGHT WITH GOD? Concluded.

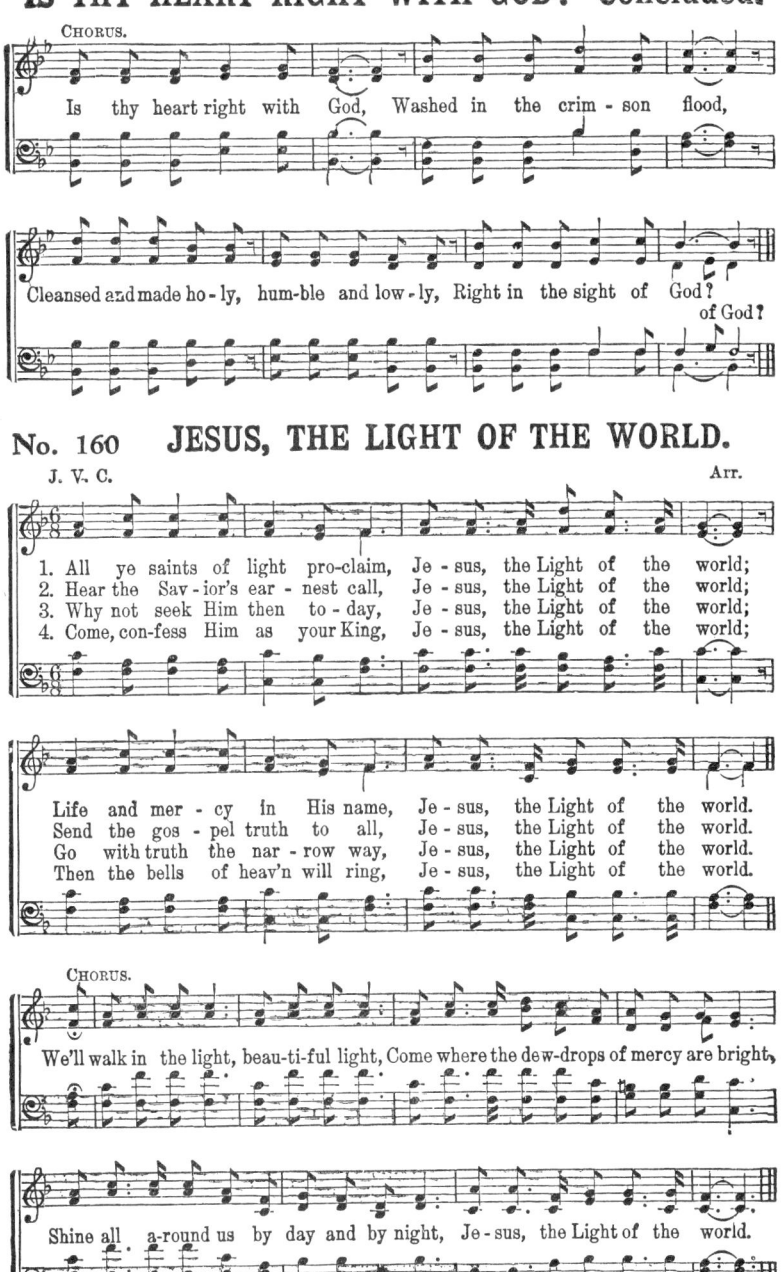

CHORUS.

Is thy heart right with God, Washed in the crim-son flood, Cleansed and made ho-ly, hum-ble and low-ly, Right in the sight of God? of God?

No. 160 JESUS, THE LIGHT OF THE WORLD.

J. V. C. Arr.

1. All ye saints of light pro-claim, Je-sus, the Light of the world;
2. Hear the Sav-ior's ear-nest call, Je-sus, the Light of the world;
3. Why not seek Him then to-day, Je-sus, the Light of the world;
4. Come, con-fess Him as your King, Je-sus, the Light of the world;

Life and mer-cy in His name, Je-sus, the Light of the world.
Send the gos-pel truth to all, Je-sus, the Light of the world.
Go with truth the nar-row way, Je-sus, the Light of the world.
Then the bells of heav'n will ring, Je-sus, the Light of the world.

CHORUS.

We'll walk in the light, beau-ti-ful light, Come where the dew-drops of mercy are bright, Shine all a-round us by day and by night, Je-sus, the Light of the world.

No. 161 ROOM FOR JESUS.

F. M. A.
F. M. ATKINSON.

1. Is there a - ny room for Je - sus, He who died on Cal - va - ry,
2. We have room for world - ly pleas - ures, Cares of life crowd ev - 'ry day,
3. Will you not make room for Je - sus, For the Christ, the cru - ci - fied?
4. Room, and time, and tho't for Je - sus, Has - ten to ac - cept His grace,

He who stand-eth, knock-ing, wait - ing, Plead - ing with you ten-der - ly?
And our hearts and minds are bur - dened, While the Lord is turned a - way.
Is there not some place to en - ter In the soul for which He died?
Ere the heart grows cold and care - less, And His pleading voice shall cease.

CHORUS.

Room for Je - sus, room for Je - sus, Let Him in your heart to-day,

Throw - ing ev - 'ry win-dow o - pen, O re-ceive Him while you may.

Copyright, 1904, by John T. Benson, Nashville, Tenn.

No. 162 THE SHELTERING ROCK.

W. E. P.
Rev. W. E. PENN.

1. There is a Rock in a wea - ry land, Its shad - ow falls on the
2. There is a Well in a des - ert plain, Its wa - ters call with en -
3. A great fold stands with its por-tals wide, The sheep a - stray on the
4. There is a cross where the Sav-iour died; His blood flow'd out in a

burn - ing sand In - vit - ing pil - grims as they pass, To
treat - ing strain, "Ho, ev - 'ry thirst - ing, sin - sick soul, Come,
moun - tain side; The Shep - herd climbs o'er moun - tains steep; He's
crim - son tide, A sac - ri - fice for sins of men, And

THE SHELTERING ROCK. Concluded.

REFRAIN.

seek a shade in the wil-der-ness. Then why will ye die? O why will ye
free-ly drink, and thou shalt be whole." Then why will ye die? O why will ye
search-ing now for His wand'ring sheep. Then why will ye die? O why will ye
free to all who will en-ter in. Then why will ye die? O why will ye

die? When the shelt'ring Rock is so near by, O why will ye die?
die? When the liv-ing Well is so near by, O why will ye die?
die? When the Shepherd's fold is so near by, O why will ye die?
die? When the crim-son cross is so near by, O why will ye die?

No. 163 **ONLY TRUST HIM.**

J. H. S. Rev. J. H. Stockton.

1. Come, ev-'ry soul by sin oppressed, There's mer-cy with the Lord,
2. For Je-sus shed His pre-cious blood Rich bless-ings to be-stow;
3. Yes, Je-sus is the Truth, the Way That leads you in-to rest;
4. Come, then, and join this ho-ly band, And on to glo-ry go,

And He will sure-ly give you rest By trust-ing in His word.
Plunge now in-to the crim-son flood That wash-es white as snow.
Be-lieve in Him with-out de-lay, And you are ful-ly blest.
To dwell in that ce-les-tial land, Where joys im-mor-tal flow.

D. S.—*He will save you, He will save you, He will save you now.*

CHORUS.

On-ly trust Him, on-ly trust Him, On-ly trust Him now;

No. 164 There's a Great Day Coming.

USED BY PER. W. L. THOMPSON & CO., EAST LIVERPOOL, O., AND THE THOMPSON MUSIC CO., CHICAGO, ILL.

W. L. T.
WILL L. THOMPSON.

1. There's a great day coming, A great day coming, There's a great day coming by and by;
2. There's a bright day coming, A bright day coming, There's a bright day coming by and by;
3. There's a sad day coming, A sad day coming, There's a sad day coming by and by;

When the saints and the sinners shall be parted right and left,
But its brightness shall only come to them that love the Lord, Are you ready for that day to come
When the sinner shall hear his doom, "Depart, I know ye not,"

CHORUS. *m pp*

Are you ready? Are you ready? Are you ready for the judgment day? For the judgment day?

No. 165 Why Do You Wait?

G. F. R.
COPYRIGHT, 1878, BY THE JOHN CHURCH CO.
GEO. F. ROOT.

1. Why do you wait, dear brother? Oh, why do you tar-ry so long?
2. What do you hope, dear brother, To gain by a fur-ther de-lay?
3. Do you not feel, dear brother, His Spir-it now striv-ing with-in?
4. Why do you wait, dear brother? The har-vest is pass-ing a-way;

Your Sav-iour is wait-ing to give you A place in His sanc-ti-fied throng.
There's no one to save you but Je-sus, There's no oth-er way but His way.
Oh, why not ac-cept His sal-va-tion, And throw off your bur-den of sin?
Your Sav-iour is long-ing to bless you; There's dan-ger and death in de-lay.

CHORUS.

Why not? why not? Why not come to Him now? now?

No. 166 **NO, NOT ONE.**

Rev. Johnston Oatman, Jr.
Geo. C. Hugg.
Slow and with feeling.

1. There's not a friend like the low-ly Je-sus, No, not one! no, not one!
2. No friend like Him is so high and ho-ly, No, not one! no, not one!
3. There's not an hour that He is not near us, No, not one! no, not one!
4. Did ev-er saint find this Friend for-sake him? No, not one! no, not one!
5. Was e'er a gift like the Sav-ior giv-en? No, not one! no, not one!

None else could heal all our soul's dis-eas-es, No, not one! no, not one!
And yet no friend is so meek and low-ly, No, not one! no, not one!
No night so dark but His love can cheer us, No, not one! no, not one!
Or sin-ner find that He would not take him? No, not one! no, not one!
Will He re-fuse us a home in heav-en? No, not one! no, not one!

D.S.—*There's not a friend like the low-ly Je-sus, No, not one! no, not one!*

CHORUS.

Je-sus knows all a-bout our struggles, He will guide till the day is done.

No. 167 **Nothing But the Blood**

Robert Lowry

1. What can wash a-way my sin? Nothing but the blood of Je-sus;
   What can make me whole a-gain? Nothing but the blood of Je-sus.
2. For my par-don, this I see— Nothing but the blood of Je-sus;
   For my cleans-ing, this my plea— Nothing but the blood of Je-sus.
3. Noth-ing can for sin a-tone, Nothing but the blood of Je-sus;
   Naught of good that I have done, Nothing but the blood of Je-sus.
4. This is all my hope and peace, Nothing but the blood of Je-sus;
   This is all my right-eous-ness, Nothing but the blood of Je-sus.

CHORUS

O precious is the flow That makes me white as snow,
No other Fount I know, (*Omit*..............) Nothing but the blood of Jesus.

No. 168   At The Cross.

Isaac Watts.   Copyright, 1885, by R. E. Hudson. Used by per.   R. E. Hudson.

1. A - las! and did my Sav-ior bleed, And did my Sov'reign die, Would He de-vote that sa-cred head For such a worm as I?
2. Was it for crimes that I have done, He groaned upon the tree, A - maz-ing pit - y, grace unknown! And love be - yond de - gree.

CHORUS.

At the cross, at the cross, where I first saw the light, And the burden of my heart rolled away, rolled away, It was there by faith I received my sight, And now I am happy all the day.

No. 169   By the Grace of God I'll Meet You.

Arr. by Woodie W. Smith.

1. O fa - thers will you meet me, O fa - thers will you meet me,
2. O moth-ers will you meet me, O moth-ers will you meet me,
3. O brothers will you meet me, O brothers will you meet me,
4. O sis - ters will you meet me, O sis - ters will you meet me,
5. O mourners will you meet me, O mourners will you meet me,

Cho. 1.—By the grace of God I'll meet you, By the grace of God I'll meet you,
Cho. 2.—There we'll shout and give Him glory, There we'll shout and give Him glo-ry.

By the Grace of God I'll Meet You. Concluded.

O fa-thers will you meet me, On Ca-naan's hap-py shore?
O moth-ers will you meet me, On Ca-naan's hap-py shore?
O brothers will you meet me, On Ca-naan's hap-py shore?
O sis-ters will you meet me, On Ca-naan's hap-py shore?
O mourners will you meet me, On Ca-naan's hap-py shore?

By the grace of God I'll meet you, On Ca-naan's hap-py shore.
There we'll shout and give Him glo - ry, For glo - ry is His own.

No. 170 Surrender All.

"But as for me and my house, we will serve the Lord."—JOSH. 24: 15.

(Copyright, 1896, by Weeden and Van De Venter. Used by per.

J. W. Van De Venter. DUET. W. S. Weeden.

1. { All to Je-sus I sur-ren-der, All to Him I free-ly give;
   { I will ev-er love and trust Him, In His pres-ence dai-ly live.
2. { All to Je-sus I sur-ren-der, Hum-bly at His feet I bow,
   { World-ly pleasures all for-sak-en, Take me, Je-sus, take me now.
3. { All to Je-sus I sur-ren-der, Make me, Sav-iour, whol-ly thine;
   { Let me feel the Ho-ly Spir-it, Tru-ly know that Thou art mine.
4. { All to Je-sus I sur-ren-der, Lord, I give my-self to Thee,
   { Fill me with Thy love and pow-er, Let Thy bless-ing fall on me.
5. { All to Je-sus I sur-ren-der, Now I feel the sa-cred flame;
   { O the joy of full sal-va-tion! Glo-ry, glo-ry to His name.

CHORUS.

I sur-ren-der all, I sur-ren-der all,
I sur-ren-der all, I sur-ren-der all,
All to Thee, my bless-ed Sav-iour, I sur-ren-der all.

No. 171

GOD CALLING YET.

"I have called, and ye have refused." PROV. 1:24.

J. BORTHWICK. JOHN.

1. God calling yet! shall I not hear? Earth's pleasures shall I still hold dear?
2. God calling yet! shall I not rise? Can I His lov-ing voice de-spise,
3. God calling yet! and shall I give No heed, but still in bond-age live?
4. God calling yet! I can-not stay; My heart I yield without de-lay;

Shall life's swift passing years all fly, And still my soul in slum-ber lie?
And base-ly His kind care re-pay? He calls me still; can I de-lay?
I wait, but He does not forsake; He calls me still; my heart, a-wake!
Vain world, farewell! from thee I part; The voice of God has reached my heart.

CHORUS.

God is call - ing, Call - ing yet,
God is call-ing yet, God is call-ing yet, God is call-ing yet, God is call-ing yet,

God is call - ing; Sinner, heed His pleading voice.
God is call-ing yet, God is call-ing yet;

This hymn is *free* to be used for the glory of God

No. 172

AMAZING GRACE.

REV. JOHN NEWTON.
Moderato.

1. A - maz - ing grace, how sweet the sound, That saved a wretch like me!
2. 'Twas grace that taught my heart to fear, And grace my fears re - lieved;
3. Thro' ma - ny dan - gers, toils and snares, I have al - read - y come;
4. The Lord has prom - ised good to me, His word my hope se - cures;

AMAZING GRACE. Concluded.

I once was lost but now am found, Was blind, but now I see.
How pre-cious did that grace ap-pear The hour I first be-lieved.
'Tis grace has bro't me safe thus far, And grace will lead me home.
He will my shield and por-tion be, As long as life en-dures.

No. 173 **O Why Not To-night?**

1. O do not let the word depart, And close thine eyes against the light, Poor sin-ner, hard-en not your heart, Be saved, O to-night.
2. To-mor-row's sun may nev-er rise, To bless thy long-de-lud-ed sight; This is the time, O then be wise, Be saved, O to-night.
3. Our Lord in pit-y lin-gers still, And wilt thou thus His love re-quite? Renounce at once your stubborn will, Be saved, O to-night.
4. Our bless-ed Lord re-fus-es none Who would, to Him their souls u-nite; Be-lieve, o-bey, the work is done, Be saved, O to-night.

CHORUS.

O why not to-night? O why not to-night? Wilt thou be saved? Then why not to-night?
O why not to-night? why not to-night? Why not to-night? why not to-night? Wilt thou be saved, wilt thou be saved? Then why not, then why not to-night?

No. 174 — ALMOST PERSUADED

P. P. B.
P. P. Bliss.

1. "Al-most per-suad-ed" now to be-lieve; "Al-most per-suad-ed" Christ to re-ceive; Seems now some soul to say, "Go, Spir-it, go thy way, Some more con-ven-ient day On thee I'll call."
2. "Al-most per-suad-ed," come, come to-day; "Al-most per-suad-ed," turn not a-way; Je-sus in-vites you here, An-gels are lin-g'ring near, Pray'rs rise from hearts so dear; O wan-d'rer, come.
3. "Al-most per-suad-ed," har-vest is past! "Al-most per-suad-ed," doom comes at last! "Al-most" can not a-vail; "Al-most" is but to fail! Sad, sad, that bit-ter wail, "Al-most, but lost."

No. 175 — The Fountain Lies Open.

Arr. by Mrs. J. T. B.

1. While the fountain lies open, The fountain lies open, Sinner, come to Jesus, and be saved.
2. O sinner, come to Jesus, O sinner, come to Jesus, Sinner, come to Jesus, and be saved.
3. For Jesus wants to save you, For Jesus wants to save you, Sinner, come to Jesus, and be saved.

No. 176 — We're Kneeling at the Mercy-Seat.

E. O. E. Arr.

1. { Just as I am, without one plea, But that Thy blood was shed for me,
   And that Thou bidd'st me come to Thee, [*Omit* . . . . .] } O Lamb of God, I come!

1st Cho.—We're kneeling at the mercy-seat, We're kneeling at the mercy-seat, Where Jesus answers pray'r.
2d Cho.—I can, I will, I do believe, I can, I will, I do believe, That Jesus saves me now.

No. 177 — O DON'T STAY AWAY.

Rev. Johnson Oatman, Jr.
Rev. W. J. Stuart, A. M.

1. Come, soul, and find thy rest, No lon-ger be dis-tressed; Come to thy Saviour's breast; O don't stay a-way.
2. Dark is the world, and cold, Her cares can-not be told; Come to thy Saviour's fold; O don't stay a-way.
3. Come with thy load of sin, Christ died thy soul to win; He will take thee in; O don't stay a-way.
4. Time, here, will soon be past, Mo-ments are fly-ing fast; Judg-ment will come at last; O don't stay a-way.
5. Come, O we pray thee, come, Come, and no lon-ger roam; Come, now, and start for home; O don't stay a-way.

CHORUS.

Prayers are as-cend-ing now, An-gels are bending now, Both worlds are blending now; O don't stay a-way.

No. 178 — HAPPY DAY.

Philip Doddridge.
E. F. Rimbault.

1. O hap-py day, that fixed my choice On Thee, my Sav-ior and my God! Well may this glowing heart rejoice, And tell its rap-tures all a-broad. Hap-py day, happy day, When Jesus wash'd my sins away! He taught me how to watch and pray, And live re-joic-ing ev-'ry day.

2 O happy bond, that seals my vows
To Him who merits all my love!
Let cheerful anthems fill His house,
While to that sacred shrine I move.

3 'Tis done; the great transaction's done!
I am my Lord's and He is mine;
He drew me, and I followed on,
Charmed to confess the voice divine.

No. 179 Pass Me Not.

Fanny J. Crosby.   W. H. Doane, Owner of Copyright. Used by Per.   W. H. Doane.

1. Pass me not, O gen-tle Sav-ior, Hear my hum-ble cry; While on oth-ers
2. Let me at a throne of mer-cy Find a sweet re-lief; Kneel-ing there in
3. Trust-ing on-ly in Thy mer-it, Would I seek Thy face; Heal my wounded
4. Thou the Spring of all my com-fort, More than life to me, Whom have I on

D. S.—*While on oth-ers*

FINE. CHORUS.   D. S.

Thou art call-ing, Do not pass me by.
deep con-tri-tion, Help my un-be-lief. Sav-ior, Sav-ior, Hear my humble cry;
bro-ken spir-it, Save me by Thy grace.
earth beside Thee? Whom in Heav'n but Thee?

Thou art call-ing, Do not pass me by.

No. 180 HOW FIRM A FOUNDATION.

1. How firm a foundation, ye saints of the Lord, Is laid for your faith in His excellent word;
2. In ev-'ry condition, in sickness and health, In poverty's vale, or abounding in wealth,
3. Fear not, I am with thee; O be not dismay'd: I, I am Thy God, and will still give thee aid;
4. E'en down to old age all my people shall prove My constant, eternal, unchangeable love;
5. The soul that on Je-sus doth lean for re-pose, I will not, I will not desert to His foes;

What more can He say, than to you He hath said, You who unto Jesus for refuge have fled?
At home or abroad, on the land, on the sea, As thy days may demand shall thy strength ever be.
I'll strengthen thee, help thee, and cause thee to stand, Upheld by my righteous, omnipotent hand.
And when hoary hairs shall their temples adorn, Like lambs they shall still on my bosom be borne.
That soul, tho' all hell should endeavor to shake, I'll nev-er, no, nev-er, no, nev-er for-sake.

No. 181   I LOVE TO TELL THE STORY.

1. I love to tell the sto-ry, Of un-seen things above, Of Je-sus and His glory
2. I love to tell the sto-ry; More won-der-ful it seems Than all the golden fancies
3. I love to tell the sto-ry; For those who know it best Seem hungering and thirsting

Of Je-sus and His love. I love to tell the sto-ry, Because I know 'tis true;
Of all our golden dreams. I love to tell the sto-ry, It did so much for me;
To hear it like the rest. And when, in scenes of glo-ry, I sing the new, new song,

CHORUS.

It sat-is-fies my long-ings, As noth-ing else can do.
And that is just the rea-son I tell it now to thee. I love to tell the sto-ry,
'Twill be the old, old sto-ry That I have loved so long.

'Twill be my theme in glo-ry, To tell the old, old sto-ry Of Je-sus and His love.

No. 182   ROCK OF AGES.

A. M. TOPLADY.   (Toplady.)   THOS. HASTINGS.
FINE.

1. Rock of A-ges, cleft for me, Let me hide my-self in Thee;
2. Could my tears for-ev-er flow, Could my zeal no lan-guor know,
3. While I draw this fleet-ing breath, When mine eyes shall close in death,

D. C.—Be of sin the doub-le cure, Save from wrath and make me pure.
In my hand no price I bring; Sim-ply to Thy cross I cling.
Rock of A-ges, cleft for me, Let me hide my-self in Thee.

D. C.

Let the wa-ter and the blood, From Thy wound-ed side which flowed,
These for sin could not a-tone; Thou must save, and Thou a-lone;
When I rise to worlds un-known, And be-hold Thee on Thy throne,

No. 183 — JESUS, SAVIOR, PILOT ME.

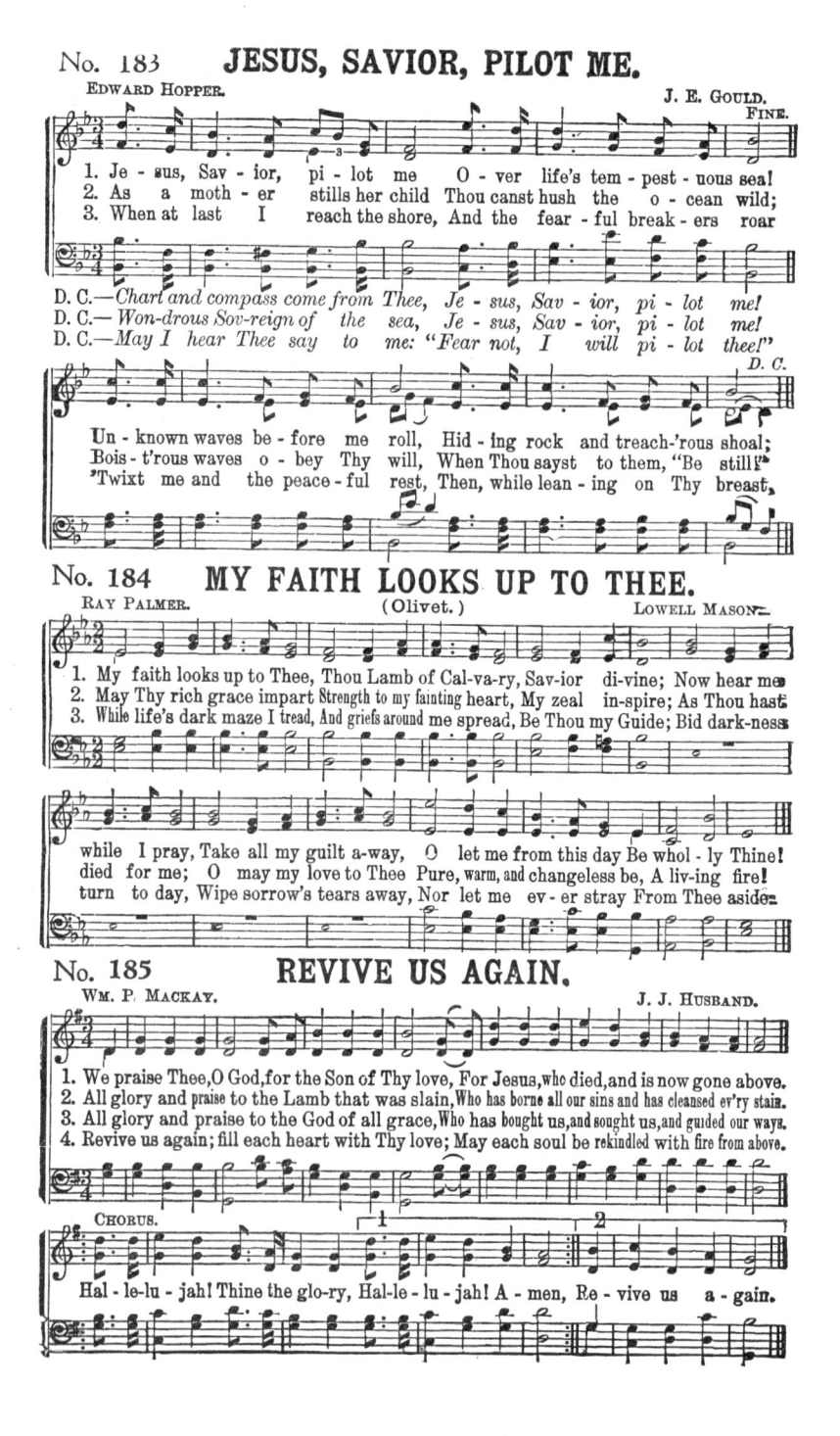

EDWARD HOPPER.
J. E. GOULD.

1. Je - sus, Sav - ior, pi - lot me O - ver life's tem - pest - uous sea!
2. As a moth - er stills her child Thou canst hush the o - cean wild;
3. When at last I reach the shore, And the fear - ful break - ers roar

D. C.—*Chart and compass come from Thee, Je - sus, Sav - ior, pi - lot me!*
D. C.—*Won-drous Sov-reign of the sea, Je - sus, Sav - ior, pi - lot me!*
D. C.—*May I hear Thee say to me: "Fear not, I will pi - lot thee!"*

Un - known waves be - fore me roll, Hid - ing rock and treach - 'rous shoal;
Bois - t'rous waves o - bey Thy will, When Thou sayst to them, "Be still!"
'Twixt me and the peace - ful rest, Then, while lean - ing on Thy breast,

No. 184 — MY FAITH LOOKS UP TO THEE.

RAY PALMER. (Olivet.) LOWELL MASON.

1. My faith looks up to Thee, Thou Lamb of Cal-va-ry, Sav-ior di-vine; Now hear me
2. May Thy rich grace impart Strength to my fainting heart, My zeal in-spire; As Thou hast
3. While life's dark maze I tread, And griefs around me spread, Be Thou my Guide; Bid dark-ness

while I pray, Take all my guilt a-way, O let me from this day Be whol - ly Thine!
died for me; O may my love to Thee Pure, warm, and changeless be, A liv-ing fire!
turn to day, Wipe sorrow's tears away, Nor let me ev - er stray From Thee aside.

No. 185 — REVIVE US AGAIN.

WM. P. MACKAY.
J. J. HUSBAND.

1. We praise Thee, O God, for the Son of Thy love, For Jesus, who died, and is now gone above.
2. All glory and praise to the Lamb that was slain, Who has borne all our sins and has cleansed ev'ry stain.
3. All glory and praise to the God of all grace, Who has bought us, and sought us, and guided our ways.
4. Revive us again; fill each heart with Thy love; May each soul be rekindled with fire from above.

CHORUS.

Hal - le - lu - jah! Thine the glo - ry, Hal - le - lu - jah! A - men, Re - vive us a - gain.

No. 186 LEANING ON THE EVERLASTING ARMS.

Rev. E. A. Hoffman.   A. J. Showalter.

1. What a fel-low-ship, what a joy di-vine, Leaning on the ev-er-last-ing arms;
   What a blessedness, what a peace is mine, Leaning on the ev-er-last - - ing arms.
2. Oh, how sweet to walk in this pilgrim way, Leaning on the ev-er-last-ing arms;
   Oh, how bright the path grows from day to day, Leaning on the everlast - - ing arms.
3. What have I to dread, what have I to fear, Leaning on the ev-er-last-ing arms;
   I have blessed peace with my Lord so near, Leaning on the ev-er - last - - ing arms.

CHORUS.

Lean - ing, lean - ing, Safe and secure from all alarms; Leaning on the everlasting arms.
Leaning on Jesus, leaning on Jesus,

Used by permission.

No. 187 Sweet By-and-By.

S. Fillmore Bennett.   BY PERMISSION.   Jos. P. Webster.

1. There's a land that is fair-er than day, And by faith we can see it a-far; For the Fa-ther waits
2. We shall sing on that beau-ti-ful shore The me-lo-di-ous songs of the blest, And our spir-its shall
3. To our boun-ti-ful Fa-ther a-bove, We will of-fer our trib-ute of praise, For the glo-ri-ous

CHORUS.

o - ver the way, To pre - pare us a dwelling place there.
sor - row no more, Not a sigh for the bless-ing of rest. In the sweet by-and-by, We shall
gift of His love, And the blessings that hallow our days.   In the sweet   by-and-by,

meet on that beautiful shore; In the sweet by-and-by, We shall meet on that beautiful shore.
by-and-by; In the sweet by-and-by,

No. 188 WE'LL WORK TILL JESUS COMES.

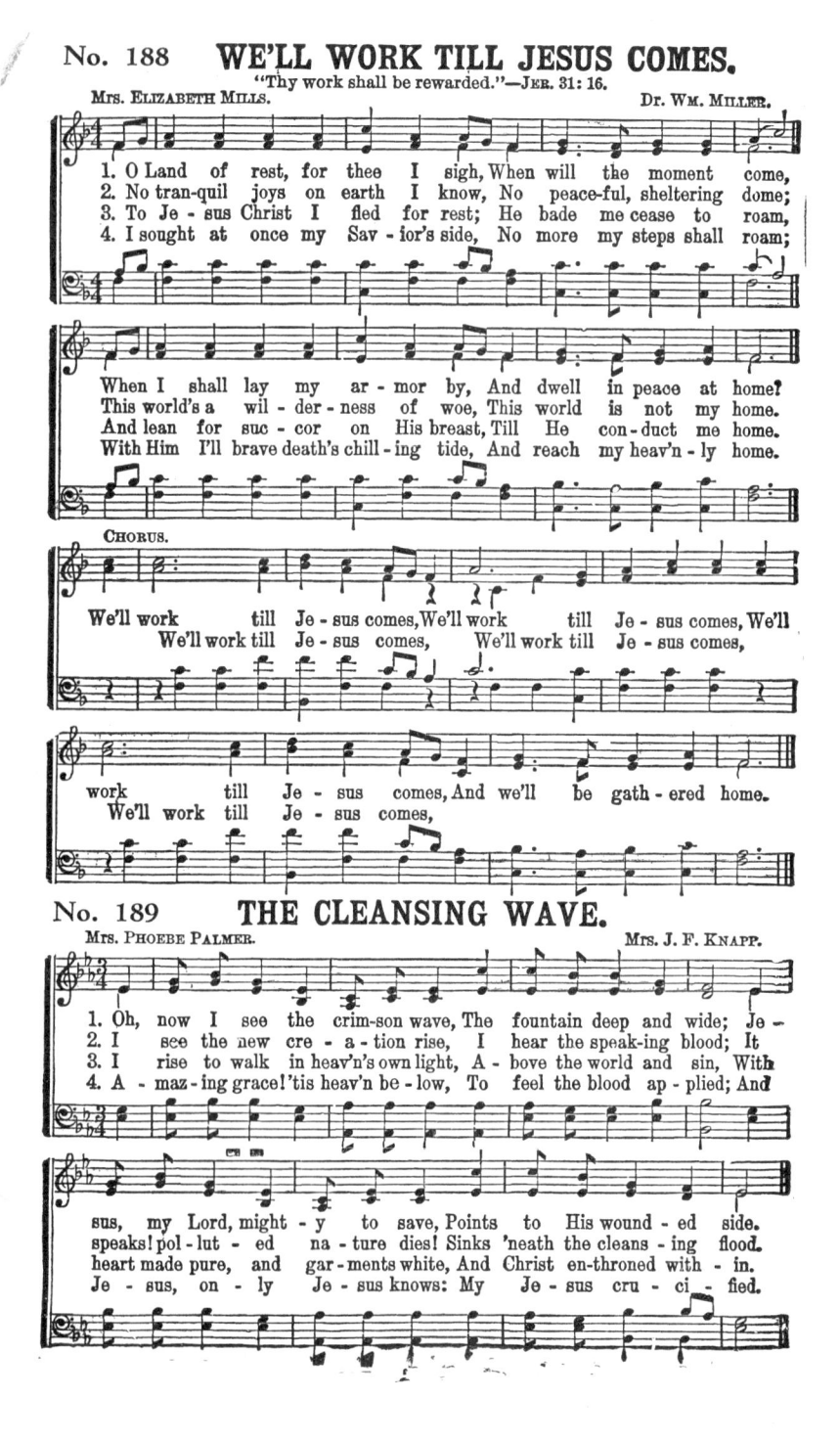

"Thy work shall be rewarded."—JER. 31: 16.

MRS. ELIZABETH MILLS.   DR. WM. MILLER.

1. O Land of rest, for thee I sigh, When will the moment come,
2. No tran-quil joys on earth I know, No peace-ful, sheltering dome;
3. To Je-sus Christ I fled for rest; He bade me cease to roam,
4. I sought at once my Sav-ior's side, No more my steps shall roam;

When I shall lay my ar-mor by, And dwell in peace at home?
This world's a wil-der-ness of woe, This world is not my home.
And lean for suc-cor on His breast, Till He con-duct me home.
With Him I'll brave death's chill-ing tide, And reach my heav'n-ly home.

CHORUS.

We'll work till Je-sus comes, We'll work till Je-sus comes, We'll
We'll work till Je-sus comes, We'll work till Je-sus comes,

work till Je-sus comes, And we'll be gath-ered home.
We'll work till Je-sus comes,

No. 189 THE CLEANSING WAVE.

MRS. PHOEBE PALMER.   MRS. J. F. KNAPP.

1. Oh, now I see the crim-son wave, The fountain deep and wide; Je-
2. I see the new cre-a-tion rise, I hear the speak-ing blood; It
3. I rise to walk in heav'n's own light, A-bove the world and sin, With
4. A-maz-ing grace! 'tis heav'n be-low, To feel the blood ap-plied; And

sus, my Lord, might-y to save, Points to His wound-ed side.
speaks! pol-lut-ed na-ture dies! Sinks 'neath the cleans-ing flood.
heart made pure, and gar-ments white, And Christ en-throned with-in.
Je-sus, on-ly Je-sus knows: My Je-sus cru-ci-fied.

THE CLEANSING WAVE. Concluded.

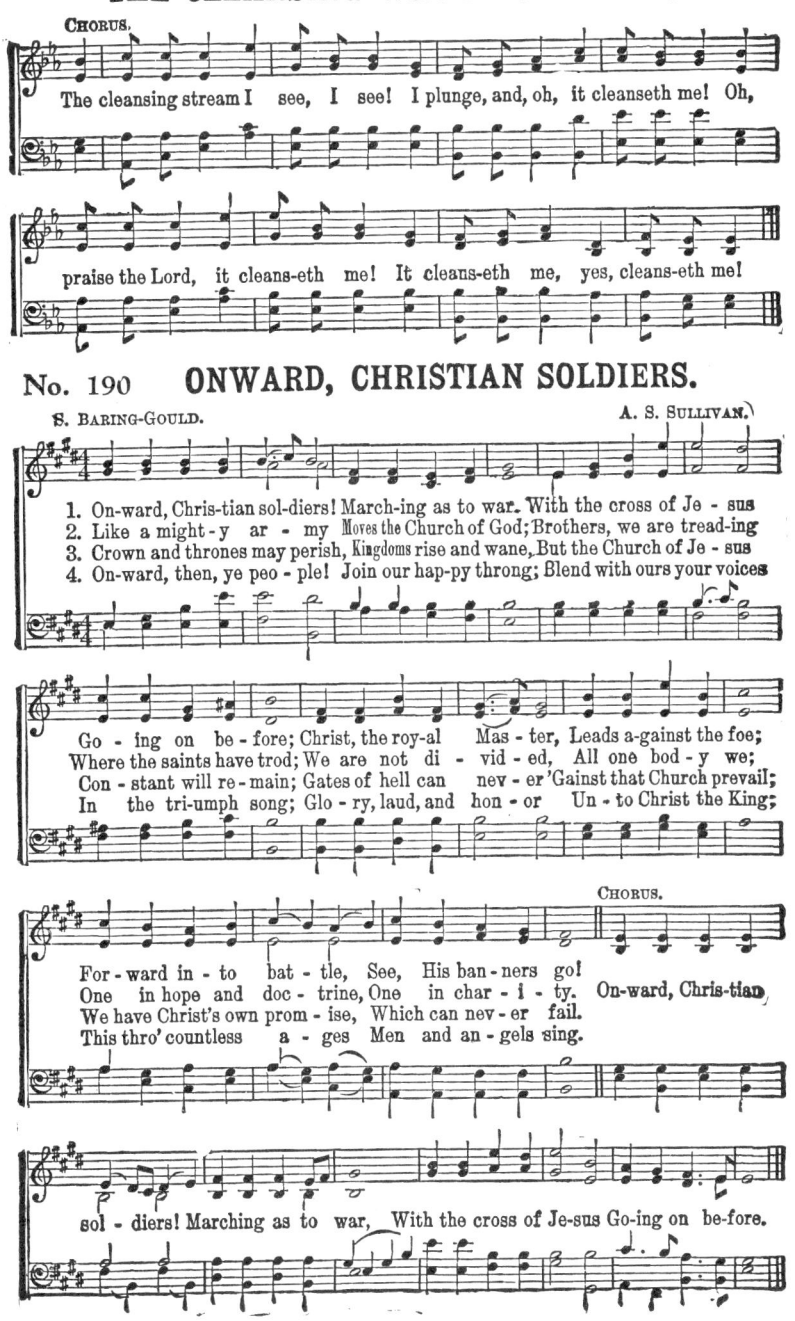

CHORUS.

The cleansing stream I see, I see! I plunge, and, oh, it cleanseth me! Oh, praise the Lord, it cleans-eth me! It cleans-eth me, yes, cleans-eth me!

No. 190 ONWARD, CHRISTIAN SOLDIERS.

S. BARING-GOULD.   A. S. SULLIVAN.

1. On-ward, Chris-tian sol-diers! March-ing as to war. With the cross of Je - sus Go - ing on be - fore; Christ, the roy-al Mas - ter, Leads a-gainst the foe; For - ward in - to bat - tle, See, His ban - ners go!
2. Like a might-y ar - my Moves the Church of God; Brothers, we are tread-ing Where the saints have trod; We are not di - vid - ed, All one bod - y we; One in hope and doc - trine, One in char - i - ty.
3. Crown and thrones may perish, Kingdoms rise and wane, But the Church of Je - sus Con - stant will re - main; Gates of hell can nev - er 'Gainst that Church prevail; We have Christ's own prom - ise, Which can nev - er fail.
4. On-ward, then, ye peo - ple! Join our hap-py throng; Blend with ours your voices In the tri-umph song; Glo - ry, laud, and hon - or Un - to Christ the King; This thro' countless a - ges Men and an - gels sing.

CHORUS.

On-ward, Chris-tian sol - diers! Marching as to war, With the cross of Je-sus Go-ing on be-fore.

No. 191 **Close to Thee.**

1. Thou, my ev - er last-ing por-tion, More than friend or life to me;
2. Not for ease or world-ly plea-sure, Nor for fame my pray'r shall be;
3. Lead me thro' the vale of shad-ows, Bear me o'er life's fit - ful sea;

D. S.—All a-long my pil-grim jour-ney, Sav-ior, let me walk with Thee.
D. S.—Gladly will I toil and suf-fer, On - ly let me walk with Thee.
D. S.—Then the gate of life e - ter - nal May I en-ter, Lord, with Thee.

Close to Thee, close to Thee, Close to Thee, close to Thee;

No. 192 **I GAVE MY LIFE FOR THEE.**

1. I gave My life for thee, My precious blood I shed, That thou might'st ransomed be, And
2. My Father's house of light, My glo-ry-cir-cled throne, I left for earthly night, For
3. I suf-fered much for thee, More than thy tongue can tell, Of bitt'rest ag-o-ny, To
4. And I have bro't to thee, Down from My home a-bove, Sal-va-tion full and free, My

quicken'd from the dead; I gave, I gave My life for thee, What hast thou given for Me?
wand'rings sad and lone; I left, I left it all for thee, Hast thou left aught for Me?
res-cue thee from hell, I've borne, I've borne it all for thee, What hast thou borne for Me?
par - don and My love; I bring, I bring rich gifts to thee, What hast thou bro't to Me?

No. 193   GLORY TO HIS NAME.

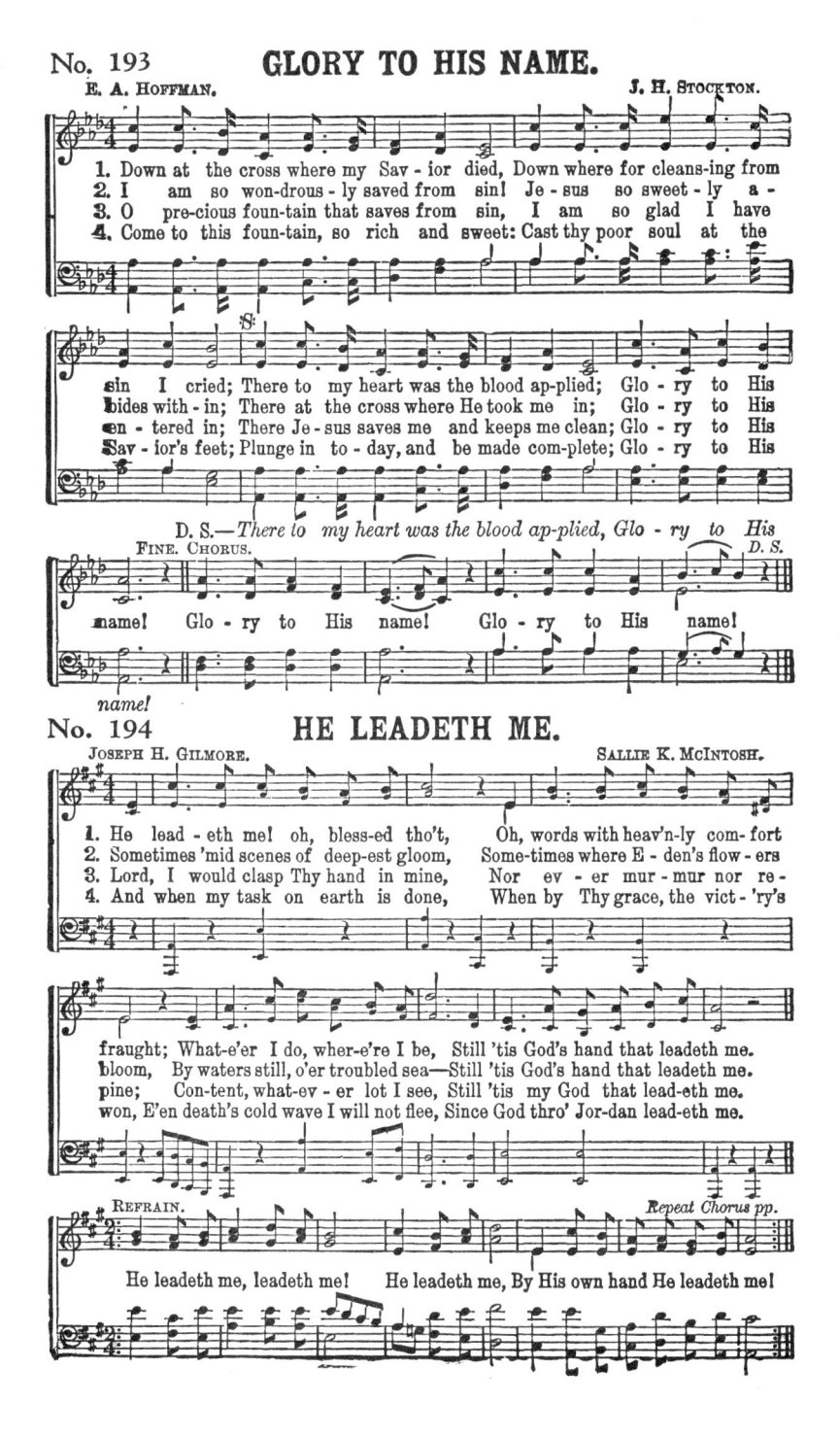

E. A. HOFFMAN.   J. H. STOCKTON.

1. Down at the cross where my Sav-ior died, Down where for cleans-ing from sin I cried; There to my heart was the blood ap-plied; Glo-ry to His name!
2. I am so won-drous-ly saved from sin! Je-sus so sweet-ly a-bides with-in; There at the cross where He took me in; Glo-ry to His name!
3. O pre-cious foun-tain that saves from sin, I am so glad I have en-tered in; There Je-sus saves me and keeps me clean; Glo-ry to His name!
4. Come to this foun-tain, so rich and sweet: Cast thy poor soul at the Sav-ior's feet; Plunge in to-day, and be made com-plete; Glo-ry to His name!

D. S.—*There to my heart was the blood ap-plied, Glo-ry to His name!*

FINE. CHORUS.

Glo-ry to His name! Glo-ry to His name!

No. 194   HE LEADETH ME.

JOSEPH H. GILMORE.   SALLIE K. McINTOSH.

1. He lead-eth me! oh, bless-ed tho't, Oh, words with heav'n-ly com-fort fraught; What-e'er I do, wher-e're I be, Still 'tis God's hand that leadeth me.
2. Sometimes 'mid scenes of deep-est gloom, Some-times where E-den's flow-ers bloom, By waters still, o'er troubled sea—Still 'tis God's hand that leadeth me.
3. Lord, I would clasp Thy hand in mine, Nor ev-er mur-mur nor re-pine; Con-tent, what-ev-er lot I see, Still 'tis my God that lead-eth me.
4. And when my task on earth is done, When by Thy grace, the vict-'ry's won, E'en death's cold wave I will not flee, Since God thro' Jor-dan lead-eth me.

REFRAIN.   *Repeat Chorus pp.*

He leadeth me, leadeth me! He leadeth me, By His own hand He leadeth me!

No. 195 — ALL HAIL THE POWER.

Rev. E. Perronet. (Coronation.) Oliver Holden.

1. All hail the pow'r of Jesus' name! Let angels prostrate fall;
Bring forth the royal diadem, And crown Him Lord of all;
Bring forth the royal diadem, And crown Him Lord of all.

2. Ye chosen seed of Israel's race, Ye ransomed from the fall;
Hail Him who saves you by His grace, And crown Him Lord of all;
Hail Him who saves you by His grace, And crown Him Lord of all.

3. Let ev'ry kindred, ev'ry tribe, On this terrestrial ball,
To Him all majesty ascribe, And crown Him Lord of all;
To Him all majesty ascribe, And crown Him Lord of all.

4. O that with yonder sacred throng We at His feet may fall;
We'll join the everlasting song, And crown Him Lord of all;
We'll join the everlasting song, And crown Him Lord of all.

No. 196 — THE SOLID ROCK.

Edward Mote. William B. Bradbury.

1. My hope is built on nothing less Than Jesus' blood and righteousness; I dare not trust the sweetest frame, But wholly lean on Jesus' name.

2. When darkness seems to veil His face I rest on His unchanging grace; In ev'ry high and stormy gale, My anchor holds within the veil.

3. His oath, His covenant, and blood, Support me in the 'whelming flood; When all around my soul gives way, He then is all my hope and stay.

Chorus.

On Christ, the solid Rock I stand; All other ground is sinking sand, All other ground is sinking sand.

No. 197 MY JESUS, I LOVE THEE.

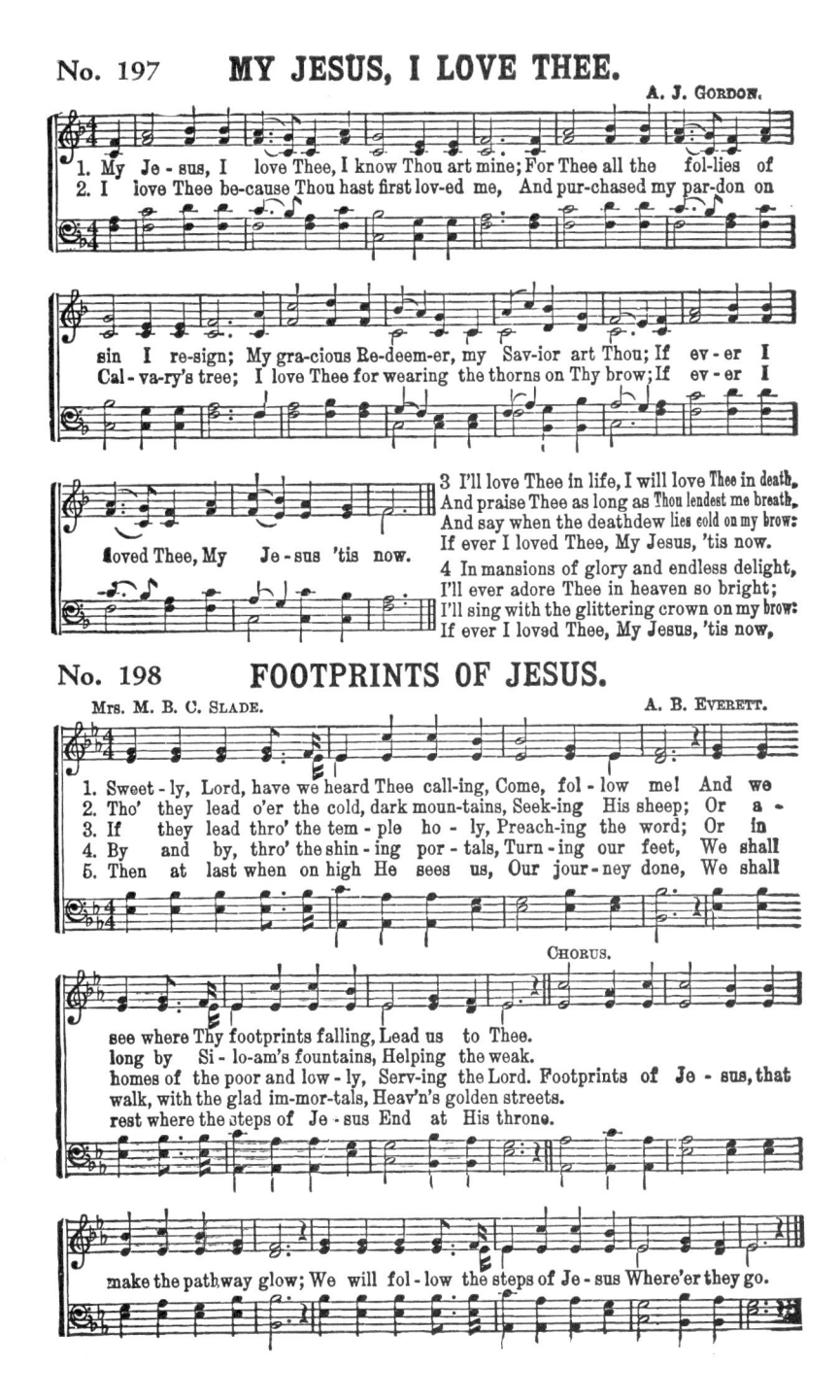

A. J. Gordon.

1. My Jesus, I love Thee, I know Thou art mine; For Thee all the follies of sin I resign; My gracious Redeemer, my Savior art Thou; If ever I loved Thee, My Jesus 'tis now.

2. I love Thee because Thou hast first loved me, And purchased my pardon on Calvary's tree; I love Thee for wearing the thorns on Thy brow; If ever I loved Thee, My Jesus 'tis now.

3. I'll love Thee in life, I will love Thee in death, And praise Thee as long as Thou lendest me breath, And say when the deathdew lies cold on my brow: If ever I loved Thee, My Jesus, 'tis now.

4. In mansions of glory and endless delight, I'll ever adore Thee in heaven so bright; I'll sing with the glittering crown on my brow: If ever I loved Thee, My Jesus, 'tis now.

No. 198 FOOTPRINTS OF JESUS.

Mrs. M. B. C. Slade.   *A. B. Everett.*

1. Sweetly, Lord, have we heard Thee calling, Come, follow me! And we see where Thy footprints falling, Lead us to Thee.

2. Tho' they lead o'er the cold, dark mountains, Seeking His sheep; Or along by Siloam's fountains, Helping the weak.

3. If they lead thro' the temple holy, Preaching the word; Or in homes of the poor and lowly, Serving the Lord.

4. By and by, thro' the shining portals, Turning our feet, We shall walk, with the glad immortals, Heav'n's golden streets.

5. Then at last when on high He sees us, Our journey done, We shall rest where the steps of Jesus End at His throne.

CHORUS.

Footprints of Jesus, that make the pathway glow; We will follow the steps of Jesus Where'er they go.

No. 199   Jesus Loves Me.
(The favorite hymn of China.)   Wm. B. Bradbury.

1. Je-sus loves me! this I know, For the Bi-ble tells me so; Lit-tle ones to Him belong, They are weak but He is strong.
2. Je-sus loves me! He who died, Heaven's gate to o-pen wide; He will wash a-way my sin, Let His lit-tle child come in.
3. Je-sus loves me! loves me still, Tho' I'm ver-y weak and ill; From His shining throne on high, Comes to watch me where I lie.
4. Je-sus loves me! He will stay Close be-side me all the way; If I love Him when I die, He will take me home on high.

CHORUS.

Yes, Jesus loves me, Yes, Je-sus loves me, Yes, Je-sus loves me, The Bi-ble tells me so.

No. 200   I'LL LIVE FOR HIM.
C. R. DUNBAR.

1. My life, my love I give to Thee, Thou Lamb of God who died for me;
2. I now be-lieve Thou dost re-ceive, For Thou hast died that I might live;

Cho.—I'll live for Him who died for me, How hap-py then my life shall be!
D. C.

Oh, may I ev-er faith-ful be, My Sav-ior and my God!
And now henceforth I'll trust in Thee, My Sav-ior and my God!

I'll live for Him who died for me, My Sav-ior and my God!

No. 201 I Know the Lord Will Make a Way

Unknown — Arranged

I know the Lord will make a way for me, I know the Lord will make a way for me;

If I walk in all the light, Shun the wrong and do the right,
If I trust and nev-er doubt, Pay my tithes and sing and shout,

I know the Lord will make a way for me.

No. 202 — SWEET HOUR OF PRAYER!

W. W. WALFORD. — W. B. BRADBURY.

1. Sweet hour of pray'r! sweet hour of pray'r! That calls me from a world of care,
And bids me at my Fath-er's throne Make all my wants and wish-es known;
In sea-sons of dis-tress and grief My soul has oft-en found re-lief,
D. S.—And oft es-caped the tempt-er's snare, By thy re-turn, sweet hour of pray'r.

2. Sweet hour of pray'r! sweet hour of pray'r! Thy wings shall my pe-ti-tion bear,
To Him whose truth and faith-ful-ness En-gage the wait-ing souls to bless;
And since He bids me seek His face, Be-lieve His word and trust His grace,
D. S.—I'll cast on Him my ev-'ry care, And wait for thee, sweet hour of pray'r.

3. Sweet hour of pray'r! sweet hour of pray'r! May I thy con-so-la-tion share,
Till from Mount Pis-gah's loft-y height I view my home and take my flight;
This robe of flesh I'll drop, and rise To seize the ev-er-last-ing prize,
D. S.—And shout, while pass-ing thro' the air, Fare-well, fare-well, sweet hour of pray'r.

No. 203 — The Great Physician.

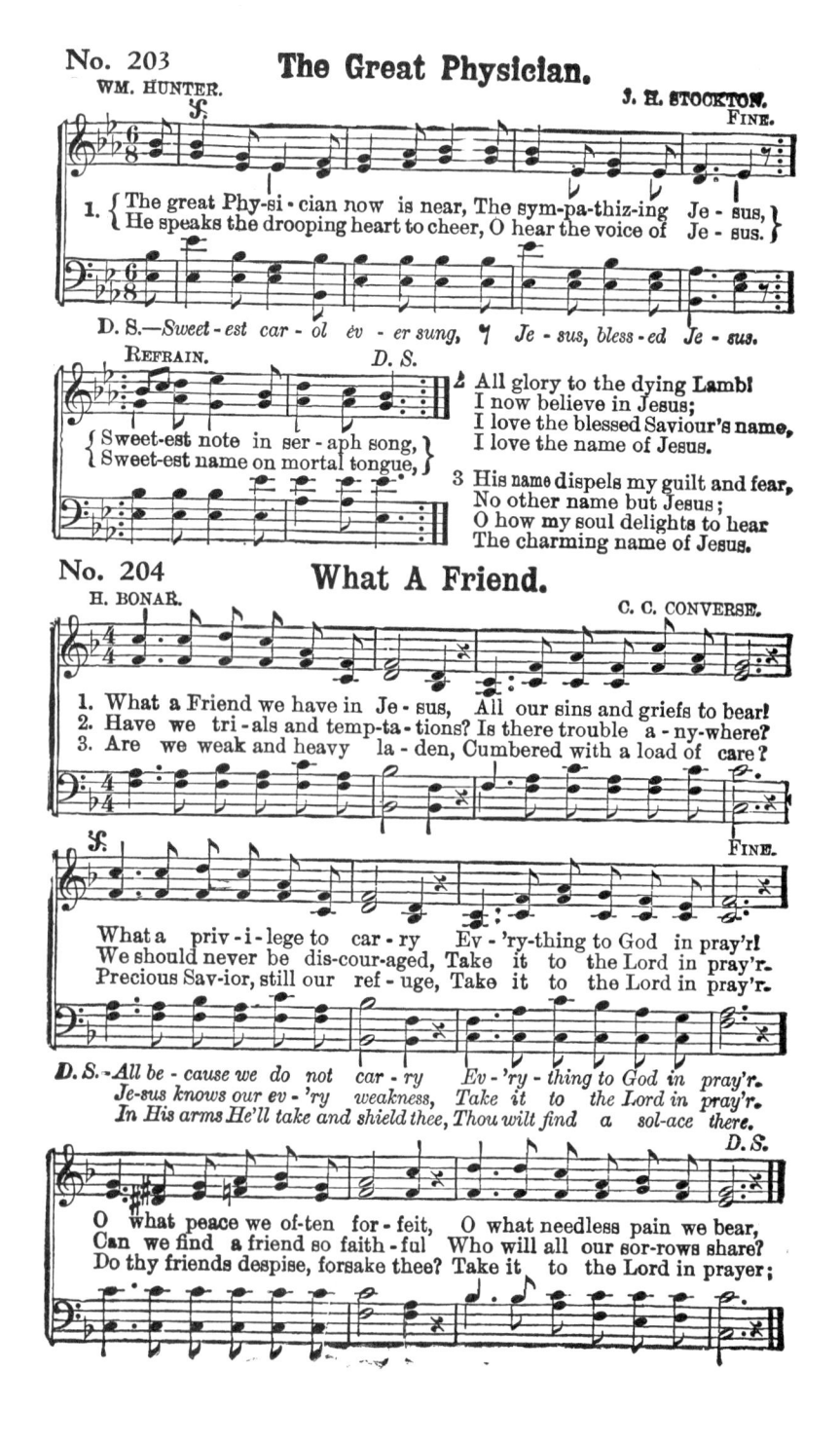

WM. HUNTER. J. H. STOCKTON.

1. The great Phy-si-cian now is near, The sym-pa-thiz-ing Je-sus,
   He speaks the drooping heart to cheer, O hear the voice of Je-sus.

D. S.—Sweet-est car-ol ev-er sung, Je-sus, bless-ed Je-sus.

REFRAIN.

Sweet-est note in ser-aph song,
Sweet-est name on mortal tongue,

2. All glory to the dying Lamb!
   I now believe in Jesus;
   I love the blessed Saviour's name,
   I love the name of Jesus.

3. His name dispels my guilt and fear,
   No other name but Jesus;
   O how my soul delights to hear
   The charming name of Jesus.

No. 204 — What A Friend.

H. BONAR. C. C. CONVERSE.

1. What a Friend we have in Je-sus, All our sins and griefs to bear!
2. Have we tri-als and temp-ta-tions? Is there trouble a-ny-where?
3. Are we weak and heavy la-den, Cumbered with a load of care?

What a priv-i-lege to car-ry Ev-'ry-thing to God in pray'r!
We should never be dis-cour-aged, Take it to the Lord in pray'r.
Precious Sav-ior, still our ref-uge, Take it to the Lord in pray'r.

D. S.—All be-cause we do not car-ry Ev-'ry-thing to God in pray'r.
Je-sus knows our ev-'ry weakness, Take it to the Lord in pray'r.
In His arms He'll take and shield thee, Thou wilt find a sol-ace there.

O what peace we of-ten for-feit, O what needless pain we bear,
Can we find a friend so faith-ful Who will all our sor-rows share?
Do thy friends despise, forsake thee? Take it to the Lord in prayer;

No. 205 GOD BE WITH YOU.

J. E. RANKIN. By per. of J. E. Rankin, owner of copyright. W. G. TOMER.

1. God be with you till we meet a-gain, By His coun-sels guide, up-hold you,
2. God be with you till we meet a-gain, 'Neath His wings protecting hide you,
3. God be with you till we meet a-gain, Keep love's banner float-ing o'er you;

With His sheep se-cure-ly fold you; God be with you till we meet a-gain!
Dai - ly man-na still pro - vide you; God be with you till we meet a-gain!
Smite death's threat'ning wave before you; God be with you till we meet a-gain!

CHORUS.
Till we meet,.... till we meet, Till we meet at Je-sus' feet;
Till we meet, till we meet a-gain, till we meet;
Till we meet..... till we meet, God be with you till we meet a-gain!
Till we meet, till we meet again,

No. 206 BLEST BE THE TIE THAT BINDS.

JOHN FAWCETT. (Dennis. S. M.) H. G. NAGELI.

1. Blest be the tie that binds Our hearts in Chris - tian love;
2. Be - fore our Fa - ther's throne We pour our ar - dent pray'r;
3. We share our mu - tual woes, Our mu - tual bur - dens bear,
4. When we a - sun - der part, It gives us in - ward pain;

The fel - low - ship of kin - dred minds Is like to that a - bove.
Our fears, our hopes, our aims are one, Our com - forts and our cares.
And oft - en for each oth - er flows The sym - pa - thiz - ing tear.
But we shall still be joined in heart, And hope to meet a - gain.

No. 207 I AM BOUND FOR THE PROMISED LAND.

REV. SAMUEL STENNETT.   DEUT. 34: 1-4.   Arr. by MRS. JNO. T. BENSON.

1. On Jor-dan's storm-y banks I stand, And cast a wish-ful eye,
To Ca-naan's fair and hap-py land, Where my pos - ses - sions lie.
2. Oh, the trans-port-ing, rapt-'rous scene, That ris - es to my sight,
Sweet fields ar - rayed in liv - ing green, And riv - ers of de - light.
3. There gen-'rous fruits that nev - er fail, On trees im - mor - tal grow;
There rocks and hills, and brooks and vales, With milk and hon - ey flow.

D. S.—*Oh, who will come and go with me? I am bound for the promised land.*

CHORUS.

I am bound for the promised land,....... I am bound for the promised land;
promised land,

4 All o'er those wide-extended plains,
Shines one eternal day;
There God the Son forever reigns,
And scatters night away.

5 No chilling winds nor poisonous breath
Can reach that healthful shore;
Sickness and sorrow, pain and death,
Are felt and feared no more.

6 When shall I reach that happy place,
And be forever blest?
When shall I see my Father's face,
And in His bosom rest?

7 Filled with delight, my raptured soul
Would here no longer stay;
Though Jordan's waves around me roll,
Fearless I'd launch away.

No. 208 JESUS LOVER OF MY SOUL.

CHARLES WESLEY.   (Martyn.)   S. B. MARSH.

1. { Je-sus, Lov-er of my soul, Let me to Thy bos-om fly, } Hide me, O my Savior
 { While the nearer waters roll, While the tempest still is high! }
2. { Oth-er ref-uge have I none. Hangs my helpless soul on Thee; } All my trust on Thee is
 { Leave, O leave me not a-lone, Still support and comfort me. }

D.C.—*Safe into the ha-ven guide, O re-ceive my soul at last.*
Cover my defenseless head With the shadow of Thy wing.

hide, Till the storm of life is past;
stayed, All my help from Thee I bring:

3 Thou, O Christ, art all I want;
More than all in Thee I find;
Raise the fallen, cheer the faint!
Heal the sick, and lead the blind!
Just and holy is Thy name,
I am all unrighteousness:
Vile and full of sin I am,
Thou art full of truth and grace,

No. 209 IS NOT THIS THE LAND OF BEULAH?

HARRIET WARNER RE QUA. REV. J. W. DADMUN.

1. I am dwelling on the mountain, Where the golden sunlight gleams O'er a land whose wondrous
2. I can see far down the mountain, Where I wandered weary years, Often hindered in my
3. I am drink-ing at the foun-tain, Where I ev- er would abide; For I've tasted life's pure
4. Tell me not of heavy cross-es, Nor the burdens hard to bear, For I've found this great sal-
5. Oh, the cross has wondrous glo-ry! Oft I've proved this to be true; When I'm in the way so

beaut-y Far ex-ceeds my fondest dreams; Where the air is pure, e-the-real, La-den
jour-ney By the ghosts of doubts and fears; Broken vows and disappointments Thickly
riv-er, And my soul is sat-is-fied; There's no thirsting for life's pleasures, Nor a-
va-tion Makes each bur-den light appear; And I love to fol-low Je-sus, Glad-ly
nar-row, I can see a path-way thro'; And how sweetly Je-sus whispers: Take the

D. S.—Is not this the land of Beulah? Blessed,

D. S. CHORUS.

with the breath of flow'rs, They are blooming by the fountain, 'Neath the amaranthine bow'rs.
sprink-led all the way, But the spir-it led, un-err-ing, To the land I hold to-day.
dorn-ing rich and gay, For I've found a richer treasure, One that fad-eth not a-way.
count-ing all but dross, World-ly hon-ors all for-sak-ing, For the glo-ry of the cross.
cross, thou need'st not fear, For I've tried the way before thee, And the glory lingers near.

bless-ed land of light; Where the flowers bloom forever, And the sun is always bright.

No. 210 A CHARGE TO KEEP I HAVE.

CHARLES WESLEY. BOYLSTON. S. M. LOWELL MASON.

1. A charge to keep I have, A God to glo-ri-fy,
2. To serve the pres-ent age, My call-ing to ful-fill,—
3. Arm me with jeal-ous care, As in Thy sight to live;
4. Help me to watch and pray, And on Thy-self re-ly,

A nev-er-dy-ing soul to save, And fit it for the sky.
Oh, may it all my pow'rs en-gage To do my Mas-ter's will.
And, oh, Thy serv-ant, Lord, pre-pare A strict ac-count to give.
As-sured, if I my trust be-tray, I shall for-ev-er die.

No. 211
FILL ME NOW.

E. H. STOKES. JNO. R. SWENEY.

1. Hov-er o'er me, Ho-ly Spir-it, Bathe my trembling heart and brow; Fill me with Thy hallowed
2. Thou canst fill me, gracious Spirit, Tho' I cannot tell Thee how; But I need Thee, greatly
3. I am weakness, full of weakness; At Thy sacred feet I bow; Blest, di-vine, e-ter-nal
4. Cleanse and comfort, bless and save me; Bathe, O bathe my heart and brow, Thou art comforting and

D. S.—Fill me with Thy hallowed

FINE. CHORUS. D. S.

presence, Come, O come and fill me now.
need Thee, Come, O come and fill me now. Fill me now, fill me now, Jesus, come and fill me now.
Spir-it, Fill with pow'r, and fill me now.
sav-ing, Thou art sweetly filling now.

presence, Come, O come and fill me now.
Copyright, 1879, by John J. Hood. By per.

No. 212
BLESSED ASSURANCE.

F. J. CROSBY. MRS. JOS. F. KNAPP.

1. { Bless-ed as-sur-ance, Je-sus is mine! O what a foretaste of glo-ry di-vine!
   { Heir of sal-va-tion, purchase of God, (Omit
2. { Per-fect sub-mission, perfect de-light, Visions of rapture now burst on my sight,
   { An-gels, descending, bring from a-bove (Omit
3. { Per-fect submission, all is at rest, I in my Saviour am happy and blest,
   { Watching and waiting, looking a-bove, (Omit

FINE. CHORUS.

Born of His Spir-it, washed in His blood.
Ech-oes of mer-cy, whispers of love. This is my sto-ry, this is my song,
Filled with His goodness, lost in His love.

D.S. Praising my Sav-iour all the day long.

D. S.

Prais-ing my Sav-iour all the day long; This is my sto-ry, this is my song,

Used by permission of Mrs. Jos. F. Knapp.

No. 213 HE LOVES ME.

ISAAC WATTS.   ARR.

1. Alas! and did my Savior bleed? And did my Sov-'reign die?
Would He devote that sacred head, For such a worm as I?

2. Was it for crimes that I have done, He groaned upon the tree?
Amazing pity! grace unknown! And love beyond degree!

3. But drops of grief can ne'er repay The debt of love I owe;
Here, Lord, I give myself away,—'Tis all that I can do.

D.S.—*He gave Himself to die for me, Because He loved me so.*

CHORUS.

He loves me, He loves me, He loves me, this I know;
I know;

No. 214 STAND UP FOR JESUS.

G. DUFFIELD.   (Webb.)   G. J. WEBB.

1. Stand up, stand up for Jesus, Ye soldiers of the cross;
Lift high the royal banner, It must not (*Omit*) suffer loss;
From vic-t'ry unto vic-t'ry His army shall He lead,

D. C.—*Till ev-'ry foe is vanquished and Christ is (Omit) Lord indeed.*

2 Stand up, stand up for Jesus,
   Stand in his strength alone;
The arm of flesh will fail you;
   Ye dare not trust your own:
Put on the gospel armor,
   And watching unto prayer;
Where duty calls, or danger,
   Be never wanting there.

3 Stand up, stand up for Jesus,
   The strife will not be long;
This day the noise of battle,
   The next the victor's song:
To him that overcometh,
   A crown of life shall be;
He with the King of glory
   Shall reign eternally.

215 Battle Hymn of the Republic.

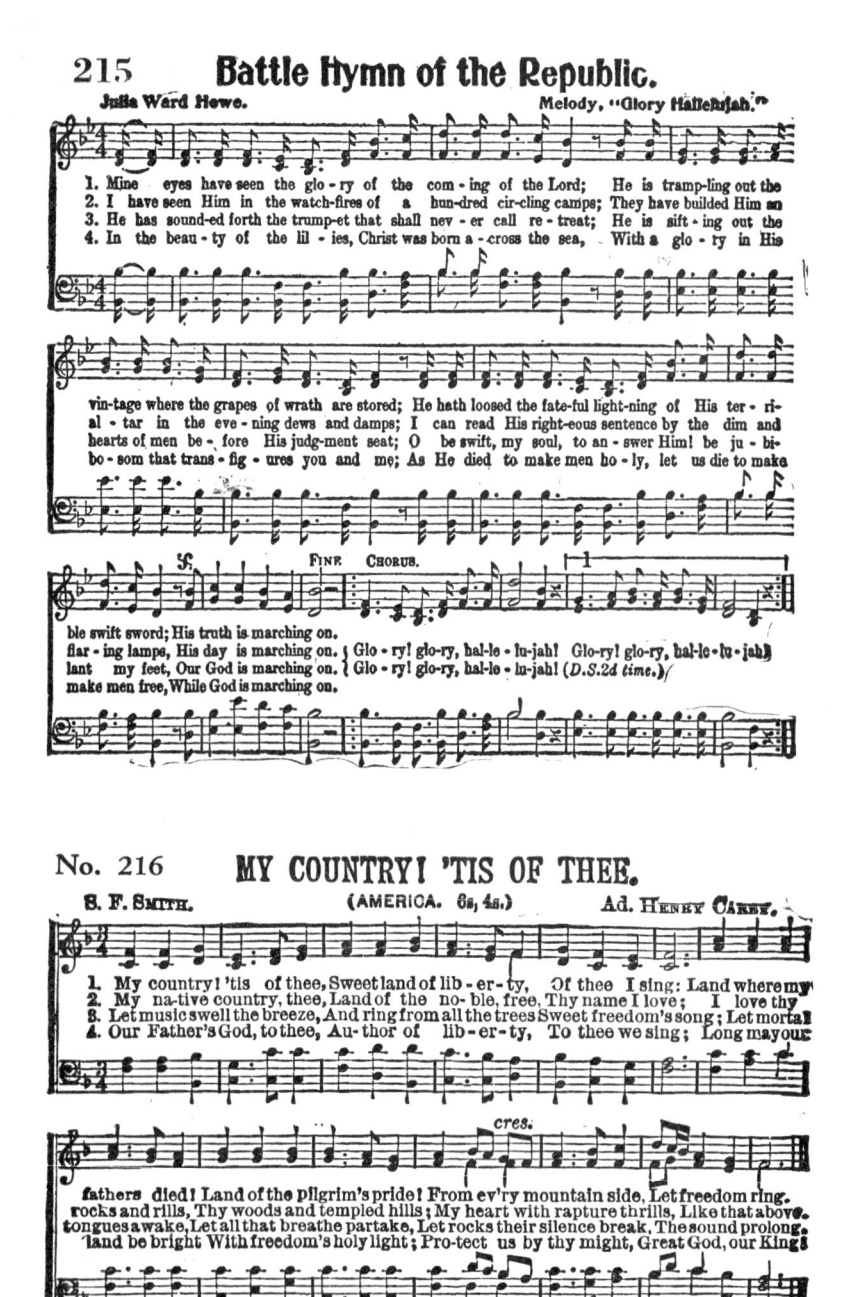

Julia Ward Howe. Melody, "Glory Hallelujah."

1. Mine eyes have seen the glo-ry of the com-ing of the Lord; He is tramp-ling out the vin-tage where the grapes of wrath are stored; He hath loosed the fate-ful light-ning of His ter-ri-ble swift sword; His truth is marching on.
2. I have seen Him in the watch-fires of a hun-dred cir-cling camps; They have builded Him an al-tar in the eve-ning dews and damps; I can read His right-eous sentence by the dim and flar-ing lamps, His day is marching on.
3. He has sound-ed forth the trump-et that shall nev-er call re-treat; He is sift-ing out the hearts of men be-fore His judg-ment seat; O be swift, my soul, to an-swer Him! be ju-bi-lant my feet, Our God is marching on.
4. In the beau-ty of the lil-ies, Christ was born a-cross the sea, With a glo-ry in His bo-som that trans-fig-ures you and me; As He died to make men ho-ly, let us die to make men free, While God is marching on.

Chorus. Glo-ry! glo-ry, hal-le-lu-jah! Glo-ry! glo-ry, hal-le-lu-jah! Glo-ry! glo-ry, hal-le-lu-jah! (*D.S. 2d time.*)

No. 216 MY COUNTRY! 'TIS OF THEE.

S. F. SMITH. (AMERICA. 6s, 4s.) Ad. HENRY CAREY.

1. My country! 'tis of thee, Sweet land of lib-er-ty, Of thee I sing: Land where my fathers died! Land of the pilgrim's pride! From ev'ry mountain side, Let freedom ring.
2. My na-tive country, thee, Land of the no-ble, free, Thy name I love; I love thy rocks and rills, Thy woods and templed hills; My heart with rapture thrills, Like that above.
3. Let music swell the breeze, And ring from all the trees Sweet freedom's song; Let mortal tongues awake, Let all that breathe partake, Let rocks their silence break, The sound prolong.
4. Our Father's God, to thee, Au-thor of lib-er-ty, To thee we sing; Long may our land be bright With freedom's holy light; Pro-tect us by thy might, Great God, our King!

INDEX

A Charge To Keep I Have	210
A Shelter in the Time of	4
A Soul Winner for Jesus	63
All Alone	85
All Hail Immanuel	143
All Hail the Power (Coro.)	195
All Hail the Power (M. L.)	129
All for Jesus	105
Almost Persuaded	174
Alone With God	119
Amazing Grace	172
Anywhere With Jesus	30
Are You Washed in the	146
At the Cross	168
Awakening Chorus	141
Battle Hymn of Republic	**215**
Beautiful	32
Blessed Assurance	212
Blest Be the Tie That Binds	206
Break Thou the Bread of Life	19
By the Grace of God I'll	169
Christ Is King	**140**
Close to Thee	191
Come and Dine	18
Come to Jesus	148
Come to the Feast	103
Come Unto Me (Jones)	72
Come Unto Me (Milam)	128
Consecrated Talents	102
Constantly Abiding	64
Covered by the Blood	91
Deeper, Deeper	**38**
Every Day and Hour	**83**
Fill Me Now	**211**
Foot Prints of Jesus	198
Glory to His Name	**193**
God Be With You	205
God Calling Yet	171
Hallelujah for the Cross	**142**
Hallelujah Praise Jehovah	130
Happy Day	178
Heavenly Sunlight	51
He Abides	40
He Brought Me Out	52
He Included Me	27
He Is Able To Deliver Thee	13
He Is Mine	144
He Keeps Me Singing	25
He Leadeth Me	194
He Lives	24
He Loves Me	213
He Ransomed Me	76
He'll Take You Through	139
He's a Wonderful Savior to	55
His Way With Thee	117
Holding On	109
Home of the Soul	65
How Firm a Foundation	180
I Am Bound for the	**207**
I Am Coming Lord	156
I Am So Glad	98
I Am Thine, O Lord	71
I Believe the Bible	78
I Feel Like Traveling On	33
I Gave My Life for Thee	192
I Hold Fast to Jesus	110
I Know the Lord Will Make	201
I Know Whom I Have	15
I Love To Tell the Story	181
I Need Jesus	28
I Never Will Cease To Love	86
I Will Make the Darkness	81
I Will Praise Him	45
I Will Sing the Wondrous	8
I Won't Have To Cross	118
I Would Not Be Denied	107
If Jesus Goes With Me	42
I'll Live for Him	200
I'll Live On	61
In the Garden	50
Is It the Crowning Day	5
Is Not This the Land of	209
Is Thy Heart Right With	159
Is Your All on the Altar	145
It Cleanseth Me	120
It Is Mine	56
It Is Truly Wonderful	66
It's So	47
Jesus Breaks Every Fetter	**157**
Jesus, I Come	116
Jesus Is Calling	151
Jesus Loves Me	199
Jesus Lover of My Soul	208
Jesus Paid It All (New)	134
Jesus Paid It All (Old)	155
Jesus Saves	108
Jesus Savior Pilot Me	183
Jesus the Light of the	160
Just As I Am	150
Lead Me Gently Home	**75**
Leaning on the Everlasting	186
Let the Lower Lights Be	73
Living by Faith	106
Love Lifted Me	11
Love Light All the Way	122
Marching on the King's	**59**
Master the Tempest Is	138
More About Jesus	49

My Burdens Rolled Away	62
My Country 'Tis of Thee	216
My Faith Looks Up to Thee	184
My Jesus I Love Thee	197
My Redeemer	94
My Sheep Know My Voice	104
My Soul Is Filled with Glory	111
'Neath the Old Olive Trees	**127**
Never Alone	113
Never Known To Fail	58
No, Not One	166
Nothing But the Blood	167
Nothing Like Jesus	88
O, Don't Stay Away	**177**
O, That Will Be Glory for Me	29
O, Why Not Tonight	173
Old Time Power	57
One Day	34
Only Trust Him	163
Onward Christian Soldiers	190
Our Lord's Return to Earth	46
Pass Me Not	**179**
Precious Memories	115
Press Along to Glory Land	90
Rapture Indeed	**14**
Redeemed	53
Rescue the Perishing	41
Revive Us Again	185
Rock of Ages	182
Room for Jesus	161
Sail On	**16**
Salvation in My Heart	152
Saved	68
Saved to the Uttermost	54
Seeking the Lost	124
Send the Light	92
Since Jesus Came Into	17
Softly and Tenderly	149
Some Bright Morning	70
Some Glad Day When Jesus	77
Sound the Battle Cry	39
Standing on the Promises	93
Stand Up for Jesus	214
Stepping in the Light	3
Such Love	6
Sunlight	31
Surrender All	170
Sunshine in the Soul	22
Sweet By and By	187
Sweet Hour of Prayer	202
Take My Life and Let It Be	**131**
Take the Name of Jesus	10
Tell It to Jesus Alone	96
Tell It Wherever You Go	20
The Cleansing Wave	189
The End Is Not Yet	82
The Fountain Lies Open	175
The Great Physician	203
The Half Has Never Been	101
The Hallelujah Side	84
The Haven of Rest	97
The Kingdom Coming	9
The Last Mile of the Way	26
The Lily of the Valley	67
The Lord Is My Shepherd	100
The Name of Jesus	44
The Old Rugged Cross	87
The Old Time Religion	158
The Rock That Is Higher	123
The Sanctifying Power	80
The Sheltering Rock	162
The Solid Rock	196
There Is a Fountain (Old)	137
There Is a Fountain (New)	136
There Is Glory in My Soul	74
There Shall Be Showers of	1
There's a Great Day Coming	164
Though Your Sins Be	36
Tidings	121
'Tis the Blessed Hour of	21
'Tis So Sweet To Trust	35
True Hearted, Whole	23
Trust and Obey	2
Unsearchable Riches	**99**
Victory in Jesus	**114**
We'll Understand It Better	**37**
We'll Work Till Jesus	188
We're Kneeling at the	176
We're Marching to Zion	95
What a Friend	204
What a Wonderful Day	112
What Did He Do	135
When I See the Blood	60
When Love Shines In	48
When the Mists Have Rolled	12
When We All Get to Heaven	79
Where He Leads Me	154
Where He Leads I'll Follow	69
Whiter Than Snow	153
Who at My Door Is Standing	147
Whosoever Meaneth Me	7
Why Do You Wait	165
Wonderful Grace of Jesus	132
Wonderful Love	125
Wonderful Peace	89
Wonderful Story of Love	126
Yield Not to Temptation	**48**